ONCE MORE FRC

ABOUT THE AUTHOR

David Bathurst was born in Guildford in 1959 and has enjoyed writing ever since childhood. Although his first book was published as long ago as 1992, it was only in 2003 that he published a work of fiction for the first time, namely *Let's Take It From The Top*; the book was sold out within a few months of publication, and, encouraged by its success, David has produced this book as a sequel.

Whilst not writing, David enjoys walking, singing and amateur dramatics. His chief claim to fame is reciting the four Gospels from memory in a single day in 1998; in 2004 he recited and sang all the surviving Gilbert & Sullivan operas from memory over a single weekend as part of the Arundel Festival. By profession David is a solicitor and legal manager of the magistrates' courts sitting at Worthing and Chichester. He lives with his wife Susan and daughter Jennifer near Chichester in West Sussex.

BY THE SAME AUTHOR

The Selsey Tram
Six Of The Best!
The Jennings Companion
Financial Penalties: Collection And Enforcement In Magistrates' Courts
Around Chichester In Old Photographs
Here's A Pretty Mess!
Magisterial Lore
The Beaten Track
Poetic Justice
Walking The Coastline Of Sussex
Best Sussex Walks
Let's Take It From The Top
Walking The Disused Railways Of Sussex

ABOUT THE SUSSEX SNOWDROP TRUST (Reg. Charity 1096622)

The Trust was set up to provide support for families in Sussex with children suffering from life-threatening or life-limiting illnesses. Applying the premise that such children are best cared for within the family home, the Trust gives financial help to affected families, provides them with nursing care and both compassionate and practical emotional support, and supplies specialist equipment to meet the day-to-day needs of the children. It relies on voluntary donations to continue its work. All profits from the sale of this book will be donated to the Trust.

ONCE MORE FROM THE TOP

By DAVID BATHURST

Illustrated by TERENCE WHITLOCK

with best wishes

2005

Romansmead Publications

First published in 2005 by

Romansmead Publications
6 Woodgate Close
Woodgate
Chichester
West Sussex PO20 3TA

Printed in England by Antony Rowe Ltd, Bumpers Farm, Chippenham, Wiltshire SN14 6LH.

British Library Cataloguing-in-Publication Data.
A catalogue record for this book is available from the British Library.

ISBN 0-9523936-4-6

PROLOGUE

Dear Katie,

A year ago I decided to record, for the benefit of my ex-girlfriend, my experiences in the choir of St Basil's. To be honest, I'd intended to stop after the first year, assuming I'd survived in the choir that long. But as my new girlfriend you have been kind enough to say how much you enjoyed the diary and how you wanted me to continue with it; and, as you will recall if you followed it to its end, my role in the choir has suddenly taken an unexpected and most interesting twist. I am being asked to coordinate a series of activities over the next year with a view to raising enough money to reroof, replaster and redecorate the choir vestry. The present structure, which was added to the existing building during what local architectural historian Gilbert Skeffington called the "late 19th century travesty of a restoration," is in a highly dangerous condition and could easily fall down of its own accord within a few years, possibly taking a fair chunk of the church with it. We have secured a lottery grant, but we are still a long way short of the total sum needed to complete the work. I feel honoured that I have been chosen to spearhead the fundraising initiative and, not having done anything like this before, I am anxious to record my progress from start to what I trust will be a successful finish. This second volume of my St Basil's choir diary will therefore concentrate not so much on the activities of the choir through the year, as my previous volume did, but will rather focus in on the fundraising efforts. Even so, I will have to rely very heavily on the support of the choir themselves, being my longest-standing acquaintances at St Basil's and likely to gain the most from the newly-built vestry, so you are still likely to read plenty of news of general choir happenings, from the major Christian festivals in the church's year such as Passiontide and Eastertide to events of really special spiritual significance such as the sale of ladies' underwear at the church's annual nearly-new bazaar.

The initiative has been driven partly by the vicar and partly by Frank Tripplehorn, our choirmaster. The vicar is quite delightful and anxious to help in any way possible, but the level of support I can expect from Tripplehorn, as I've called him in my previous diary, is much harder to gauge. He likes to think of himself as a good selfless musician constantly in pursuit of the highest vocal standards and keen to encourage young talent. Much of the time his commitment to excellence is very evident, but occasionally it is tinged with thoughtlessness that can border on hurtfulness; he has a caustic wit, and docs not always have regard for the feelings of others. And it's difficult to see how his retention of Cora Willoughby-Smith and Hazel Ledworthy in the choir sits with his assertion that he had no time for choir members with the vocal aptitude of tripe fritters. At his suggestion, I tried to speak to all the choir members over the phone or at the New Year's Eve party to tell them a little about my new role in the choir and what I hoped they would be able to do for me. Not surprisingly, the party hostess Rachel Ellis (soprano), her husband Brian (bass) and Brian's fellow bass Ken Foulkes, all smashing people, are right behind me. Eileen Crosby (alto) is less obviously enthusiastic but I think quietly supportive in her way. Margaret Pardew (soprano), of more evangelical persuasion, has already put me on her Prayer List which she keeps on the wall in her kitchen next to her Thought For The Day calendar and her mother's red gas and electricity bills. Alison Sparkes and her daughter Zoe, both also sopranos, seem rather too busy with Zoe's constant school activities, from Saturday morning basketball to Sunday evening rollerblading, to show a great deal of interest, but Zoe's brother and our only true treble, mischievous Matthew, has already given me a whole host of sponsorship ideas, from juggling with chipmunks in the central reservation of the M25 to standing on top of Nelson's Column eating a bag of jam doughnuts. The other ladies are altogether less committed. Cora Willoughby-Smith, soprano and prima donna of the choir, seemed disappointed that I'd not immediately asked her to organise one of her Hungry For Opera evenings, consisting of a five-course candlelit meal with her attempting to sing one of the classic deathbed arias from grand opera between each course. Hazel Ledworthy (alto) simply looked at me as though I had suggested we all started singing the services in Kurdish with nothing on save figleaves to cover up the deficiencies in our canticles. Joan Trumpington (alto), the hopelessly inefficient choir secretary, said she would be happy to help with PR, although previous experience suggests that if left to her own devices an invitation to St Basil's church hall at 7.30pm on May 25th will be so translated on to her publicity material that the supporters of the event will be lining up at 2.45am on December 9th outside number 27A Thor Heyerdahl Street, Trondheim. And Lesley Markwick (soprano), not one to suffer fools gladly, said she could cope with a quiz evening or a beetle drive, but not a repetition of the last church fundraising event she remembered, a Scottish dancing evening compered by Jock McSporran, alias sidesman Tony Pratt, who after six abortive runthroughs, three rounds of drinks and a chicken making an unusually determined effort to fight its way out of a basket, had still failed to make anyone strip a willow, or indeed get to the bottom of Gay Gordon.

As far as the other men are concerned, I couldn't get hold of Craig Dumbleton (tenor) over the New Year, but I'm quite certain he can oblige me if, as part of my fundraising campaign, I ever wish to organise a quiz on railway station architecture on the Southern Region in the 1950's or hold a special edition of *Mastermind* with the Rise And Fall Of The Furry Parka Anorak, 1971-1975, as an acceptable specialist subject. My other fellow tenor, Arthur Ramsbottom, has an atrocious unblendable voice but as the self-appointed choir archivist he's indicated he's happy to record any fundraising efforts for posterity. His previous choir videos can of course tell me what stunts have been tried before and what can be relied upon to be a complete disaster; I've already begun to get some idea, having seen footage of the choir outing in 1981 and the Great Margate Curried Whelk Eating Contest. The cooperation of the two basses I've mentioned is offset by a distinctly negative attitude on the part of the other two. Irving Cattermole, a laconic man of few words with a cynical misanthropic view on life in general, said that as soon as the new vestry was in place some other part of the church would be falling down and wouldn't it be much simpler to invite one of the youths on the Pheasantmead Estate to come and torch the whole place, thereby enabling us to start afresh with a brand new building on the insurance money. Lastly, Henry Peasgood, whose motto in life is "Anything you can do, I can do better," and who considers himself to be God's special gift to music making at St Basil's, has said he's likely to be far too busy to lend his hand to anything as humdrum as fundraising but if he has a spare moment he will try and call up his old friend "John R" to compose a special anthem for us which could somehow be marketed to raise money. He then made some excuse and left so I was quite unable to work out if he meant John Rutter, the famous composer and conductor, or John Roper, the local butcher who appeared on local radio two days ago playing his very own Symphony Number 1 for Single Potato Chip And Length Of Bubble Wrap.

JANUARY

Friday 3rd January

Several absentees tonight and a real post-Christmas flat feel to our practice for Sunday's Epiphany service. The thought of organising summer fairs, open-air concerts and evening barbecues seemed laughable as we emerged from our shorter than usual rehearsal into perishing cold and bitter wind.

We decided to cheer ourselves up with a drink at the Holly Tree. Arthur Ramsbottom was standing beside me at the bar waiting to order, and I remarked to him that everyone still seemed seasonally demotivated. I expected little more than a polite grunt in response, but to my surprise his eyes lit up and he spoke. "I suppose if you're after a fundraising vehicle, I could write a choir history," he said. "It'd take me a few months, and I've no facilities to typeset it, but I'd get it done in time for us to put it out as a stocking-filler for next Christmas."

I thanked him, of course, and said if he didn't have access to a PC I'd be pleased to type it up for him, but as I returned to the others with my drinks I really did wonder if anyone would be so interested in choir goings-on as to make its history saleable amongst a circle wider than those likely to be mentioned in it. Judging by the reaction of others on my table, I wasn't the only one. Tripplehorn in particular thought Arthur's proposal was hilarious. "I can just see them queuing to read his immortal prose," he sniggered. "The day Mrs Fitzherbert's pencil sharpener nearly fell down the grating in the north transept. The sensational discovery of a smear of lipstick in Mrs Troutbeck's copy of *Hymns Ancient And Modern*. Or Mr Hartridge confiscating Bobby McBride's gobstoppers after he was caught sucking one during evensong on the second Sunday after Lammas Day in 1958." Whereupon Arthur Ramsbottom appeared, looking somewhat put out, and muttered something about not bandying his material about in quite such a cavalier manner.

Tripplehorn sheepishly apologised for being so indiscreet.

"Thank you," Arthur replied stiffly. "It was actually the third Sunday after Lammas Day. In 1961."

If I see a huddle of nervous-looking individuals camped outside his house over the next few days, I shall know it's the major newspaper editors desperate to secure the exclusive serialisation rights.

Epiphany Sunday 5th January

Before the service this morning I received the agenda for Tuesday night's PCC meeting. Having agreed to give up my place on the PCC to Tripplehorn, I was delighted to pass the agenda on to him, not in the least bit conscience stricken by his assertion, in response to Rachel's enquiry as to whether he was looking forward to attending, that he would rather be forced to suck cow dung off Albert Peabody's electric fence.

I hoped that a few members of the choir besides Arthur might have produced some fundraising ideas that would at least tide us over the winter months, but the silence was deafening.

Over coffee, however, Matthew came bounding up to me and said "I hear we're bringing out a book for Christmas. What about a church choir joke book?"

I'm sure there are plenty of stories and jokes about church choir life in general with which I could perhaps spice up Arthur's prose, but off the top of my head I couldn't recall any whatsoever, so I asked Matthew to give me an example.

"All right," he said, "what's black and white and red all over?"

Resisting the temptation to give the obvious answer I said I had no idea.

"A sunburnt penguin!" he chortled.

"And what's that got to do with the choir?" I asked him.

"Oh, nothing," he said. "I just like the joke, that's all."

Fortunately, perhaps, Alison prised him away before I was able to enquire of him what part of "as much use as a teacosy in an elephant house" he didn't understand.

Friday 10th January

My doubts about the viability of Arthur's book, the first part of which I'd been promised today or tomorrow, had not lessened at all during the week. Indeed, had I received any suggestions of further fundraising ideas at tonight's choir practice, I would probably have binned the project forthwith. In fact, Arthur was away with bronchitis, so not only did I have a much more enjoyable evening's singing but I was able to be more candid than I might perhaps otherwise have been when asked for my thoughts on his project. Everyone agreed that the undertaking required a very considerable financial outlay and the potential loss was enormous.

"If you want my advice," said Henry Peasgood, "steer clear of the so-called vanity presses. The ones that charge you to have the book typeset, bound and printed and then just pay you the royalties. A good friend of mine, a brilliant musician, almost bankrupted himself that way. He followed up an ad in one of the Sunday papers and sent in his script. The publishers said it'd be a sure-fire winner. Would sell thousands and the big royalty cheques would easily clear the publishers' bills. So he paid them what amounted to his life savings. I think they managed to sell ten copies. The royalty cheque just about covered the cost of the phone calls to remind them that the cheque was due. My friend had to remortgage his

house, sell his car, everything. And all for wanting to make his brilliant work of scholarship available to a wider audience."
I asked him what the book was called.
"The Use Of The Modulation To The Relative Minor In Late 18th Century Spanish Neo-Renaissance Choral Composition," replied Henry Peasgood. Next time I want helpful advice on project planning, I'll stick to more reliable sources. Either the leaves inside my bargain pack of Happy Shopper teabags, or Mystic Mildred, psychic phenomenon and fount of spiritual enlightenment. Well, to readers of her horoscope column on the Coffee Break page in our local free newspaper, at any rate.

Saturday 11th January

An intriguingly thick envelope in today's post, which I opened to find what at first glance appeared to be a very long handwritten letter. I didn't recognise the handwriting and immediately ruled out my two regular lengthy correspondents, namely my uncle Reg who leads safaris in the Serengeti and my dad's cousin George who drives buses in Deptford. It turned out, on closer examination, to be Arthur's jottings on the history of St Basil's choir. Although some parts were rather hard to read, the style appeared succinct and, crucially, the text seemed quite a bit shorter than I'd expected or indeed feared. He'd dealt with the entire war years in just a couple of lines, and his analysis of the 1960's, including the feud between the organist Wilson Fazackerley and first soprano Amelia Godbold, was positively snappish. His accounts of some of the more memorable choir outings were admirably concise, and charitably he'd made no mention of my getting left behind by the coach on the last one. The whole thing came to no more than twelve sides of A4. That made it a little short for a proper book, but I reflected that it would still provide plenty of reading material which once properly typed could be made into a nice affordable booklet, perhaps with a few photos as well.
I met up with Katie in town this morning and we enjoyed coffee and cakes in my favourite of the town's many cafes, while speculating on possible eye-catching titles for the book. Katie reminded me of a notice she'd seen, she thinks possibly on *That's Life*, promoting a talk given by a local church entitled WHAT IS HELL LIKE? and, underneath in only slightly smaller letters, the invitation to COME AND HEAR OUR CHOIR. For a working title, I think we could do a lot worse. Katie was having to work this afternoon, so after a brisk walk in the pleasant January sunshine, I decided to go home and bash out Arthur's work on my PC. I actually created the file under the name WHAT IS HELL LIKE? and headed the first page with it.
Two hours later, I was beginning to have the question answered for myself. Arthur's writing wasn't completely illegible but there were

numerous asterisks, afterthoughts, and directions such as "go to page four" which since half the pages weren't numbered made the exercise doubly difficult. As for punctuation, Arthur seemed not to have heard of the comma, let alone the full stop. Still, three hours later I got there, and having carefully saved it both to disk and hard drive, flopped down for a well-earned rest before Katie came round for the evening.

We were enjoying a quiet, romantic dinner when the phone rang. It was Arthur, wanting to check I'd safely received the package. I told him I had, and everything was well in hand.

"Splendid," he said. "I'll try and have the first chapter done by the end of the month."

"What do you mean?" I asked him. "I thought you'd sent me the whole thing."

"Oh, Lord, no," he replied. "That was just the preface."

Sunday 12th January

Before the service today, Rachel introduced me to a friend of hers named Steve who she said would be joining me on the tenor line this morning. He told me he was a trained professional singer and had only quit the music business on realising that salary and job prospects were rather better as a plumber. Apparently he's doing a major job in the area and because he lives over two hundred miles away he's rented the mansion belonging to Brigadier Whittlesford who's currently abroad, whilst carrying out the work. Rachel, bless her, had persuaded him to come and join us in the choir while he's staying down here. On the strength of the Gloria, psalm and Gospel acclamation it was clear he had a tremendously good voice. He also appeared to have a good sense of humour: pointing out to me that the tune for the second hymn this morning was entitled Redhead No 46, he observed "If that's the best the composer could come up with after 46 of them, perhaps he ought to try a brunette."

It got better after the service. We told Steve about our fundraising campaign and he's offered us the use of the house he's renting for an indoor games evening on the 25th of this month for choir members, their families and friends in aid of the vestry fund. Apparently he's discovered a table tennis table and a snooker table sitting folded up in the garage, and has suggested that choir members could bring board games and playing cards on the night so that there really are games to suit everyone's tastes. Although the exact logistics have to be decided, it is great to have another fundraising vehicle so quickly.

Katie was most upset that having had to interrupt our dinner last night to deal with Arthur's phone call, I felt obliged to devote a good part of our afternoon together to assembling plans for the games evening. I told her I wasn't happy either but it had to be sorted out. Perhaps I should try hymn tune writing as a source of income instead. Sedentary and uncomplicated. To say nothing of all those redheads.

Tuesday 14th January

Tripplehorn rang and asked if I'd help him and Joan Trumpington with the annual tidy and clear-out of the choir music cupboard. "There'll be something in it for you, I promise you," he said to me. On my way down to the church I wondered what this might be, deciding that even if a new Ferrari or widescreen TV were a little too much to hope for, an indefinite sabbatical for Arthur Ramsbottom would be equally acceptable. When I got there, however, Tripplehorn merely told me he believed there might be some music in the cupboard that was worth selling to dealers, thereby making some money for the vestry.

Unfortunately it became clear that, on preliminary viewing of the cupboard's contents, anything worth offering to dealers was stuff Tripplehorn would want to keep anyway and the rest was worthless rubbish. In fact, Tripplehorn reckoned we'd make more money pulping the lot and setting up our own recycling plant in the churchyard. However, since, in his words, that would involve the PCC actually having to make a decision, he suggested we might as well bin the useless material and get home in time for *Tonight With Trevor McDonald*. "I mean, look at this junk," he said irritably, snatching at a few pieces at random. "*Merrily Prime Your Playful Sitar* by Doctor Samuel Boggis. *Fill The Cup With Gilead's Balm* by Percy Luffington. *When Joseph Plucked The Scented Wheat* by Cyril Chetwynd Dibble. We might as well try flogging it to the local curry house."

I told him we ought to save that for Thomas Weelkes' madrigal *As Vesta Was From Latmos Hill Descending* but he claimed not to know what I was on about.

Despite the purge we'd had this time last year, there seemed to be even more for the dustmen this time, including a number of works that we could have sworn we'd thrown out last year. But we worked away with determination, and two hours later our sturdy black bin-liner was full to bursting with lovingly composed pieces that were now consigned to history as far as St Basil's was concerned. "Wonderfully strong, these bin-liners," remarked Tripplehorn. "Can use them again and again."

"That's right," said Joan. "I think this is the very same bag that contained all that music that I spent a week putting in the cupboard last summer."

"And where did you find all that music in the first place?" Tripplehorn enquired.

"Oh, it was just lying in the vestry by the waste-paper bin," said Joan, "and one of the cleaners told me it made the vestry look messy. So I got it all out and filed it. I assumed it was stuff you'd ordered in yourself."

"So let's get this right," said Tripplehorn. "We've just spent an entire evening putting into a black bin-liner for the dustmen the same music that we put into a black bin-liner for the dustmen a year ago."

He picked up the full bin-liner and for one horrible moment I thought he was going to decapitate Joan with it, but thankfully sanity prevailed and he settled for hurling it out of the back door of the vestry. Only for an anguished and unmistakably feline squeal to ensue, with confirmation soon following that Gilead's balm and Joseph's scented wheat had made a direct hit on Sir Galahad The Ninth, Millicent Treadwell's ageing ginger tom.

The emergency vet did a splendid job at reasonable cost and as I'd videoed Trevor McDonald I was able to watch him when I finally made it home at ten to midnight. All the same, I think if asked to have another purge on the choir music cupboard, even if a Ferrari really is on offer, I'll settle for a quiet night in. And follow Dr Boggis' instruction to merrily prime my playful sitar.

Friday 17ᵗʰ January

Exciting news at tonight's practice. We've been invited to sing evensong at Exeter Cathedral on Pentecost Sunday and there's even talk of our giving the first performance of a brand new Pentecost anthem at the service. But Tripplehorn's nit-picky mood as we rehearsed for Sunday's music jolted us out of any complacency we might have felt upon hearing the invitation. I could tell he was on the warpath, right from the moment that his request for volunteers to help prepare the games room at Brigadier Whittlesford's in readiness for next Saturday met with total silence. Frankly I didn't see why I should offer my services, having done all the legwork on the games evening so far, but that didn't stop me feeling somewhat uncomfortable as Tripplehorn took out his frustrations on Matthew, summarily confiscating the packet of sherbet bon-bons from which he had been liberally helping himself during the first four run-throughs of the first two sections of Sunday's psalm chant. We proceeded to make a dreadful mess of the motet, and it was at this point that Tripplehorn finally snapped and inflicted his nastiest sanction, namely getting us all to sing a piece of the motet individually, and informing us that whoever made the worst job of it would be automatically volunteered to set up the games room.

His threat certainly had the desired effect, and all the sopranos and altos succeeded in singing the piece required of them to a passable standard. The basses also acquitted themselves reasonably well, as did Craig and Arthur. When it came to me, the last to have to do it, Tripplehorn asked me to "go from 25."

He gave me a note, but inexplicably I was quite unable to pick up my part from it.

"Right, that's it," he said to me, after my solo rendition spluttered to a halt as rapidly as an inadequately de-iced Lada on a frosty morning. "The job's yours. I'll leave it to you to arrange with Steve when you'll go round to set up, and who you'll get to help you."

As we continued work on the piece, I realised that I'd misunderstood him and gone from the start of page 25 rather than bar 25. Then again, he was only joking about my having to do the setting-up, and even if he wasn't, which he was, it's still not for him to dictate to anyone how they choose to spend their leisure time, nor to impose totally inappropriate sanctions for a minor musical error, and frankly if he thinks I'm having my weekend arrangements decided for me in such arbitrary fashion, he's got another think coming.

Having said that, I've not actually planned anything for Sunday afternoon. So I'll probably end up doing it anyway.

Slightly concerned that, when the subject came up, at least three people asked "What games evening?" This after I'd spent much of Monday night preparing and sending a circular letter to the choir advertising it, urging them to bring family and friends, and asking for the loan of board games. Perhaps it wasn't a good idea to entrust Joan with the task of sending the letters. They're probably only just arriving now. At the left-luggage office of the Grand Central Station, Shanghai.

Sunday 19th January

I had intended after this morning's service to corner each choir member individually to get their support for the games evening. I had just persuaded Brian to come and give me a hand this afternoon, but before I could get the chance to speak to anyone else I was approached by Queenie Haverthwaite's son. He told me that among his late mother's personal effects was a very impressive collection of books, most of which he said were destined for second-hand bookshops and charity shops, but which he's now prepared to offer to us for our fundraising. I've promised to go over on Wednesday to look at them. It was of course great to have this further boost to our vestry fund, but by the time we'd made the arrangements, there was nobody left to tell about the games evening.

Meanwhile, this afternoon it was round with Brian to Brigadier Whittlesford's, for what I hoped would be a reasonably quick job. It was a shame Steve himself couldn't assist, but after having sung beautifully again with us this morning, he'd had to get on with his contract and was forced to leave us to it.

To my surprise, Henry Peasgood was already there. "I've got some good news," he announced. "I've found a whole cupboard's worth of board games and I've got them here with me this afternoon."

"Excellent," I said.

"There's bad news as well," he went on hastily. "I don't think any of them have been played since about 1965. They'll all need sorting out so that we're sure everything's there that should be. I would offer to do it myself, but I just haven't got the time this week."

And as if the prospect of this hefty additional inroad into my coming week's leisure time was not ghastly enough, there was then even worse news to follow: firstly that Henry was arranging an unspecified "surprise item" to round off the games evening, and secondly that he'd brought with him his two teenage nephews to help set up this afternoon. As a result, the whole operation took twice as long as it would have done had Brian and I just got on with it ourselves. I'm not sure what proved the most gruesome aspect of the whole business: the splinters which macheted their way unerringly inside my finger nails; the excruciating creak of the folding legs of the snooker table which reminded me of the documentary I'd been watching two nights before on medieval instruments of torture; the failure of the younger nephew to hold his corner of the ping-pong table for the 20 seconds I'd asked him to, causing another corner to come crashing down on my foot; or the quotations by the nephews of so much of the previous night's episode of *Sex And The City* that by the end I felt I knew the lines better than the scriptwriters themselves.

And that was before going home and sorting out the board games. Whatever remedies are advocated by psychotherapists for inner spiritual healing of recent victims of maverick table tennis tables, I doubt they include sitting up until ten past midnight double-checking that Mr Bun the Baker is safely ensconced in the Happy Families pack and that there is sufficient currency within the Monopoly set to finance something more upmarket than the metropolitan sewage works.

Wednesday 22nd January

Quite a positive day, really. Taking advantage of a slack fifteen minutes at work, I was able to make arrangements for the transfer of Queenie's book collection to Fred Robinson, a friend of a member of our congregation, who owns a second-hand bookshop at the far end of town. He will keep the books he feels he can sell and will give me a cheque for those, and he will then divide the remainder evenly between the town's charity shops. He also put me in touch with an acquaintance of his, Lionel Harbottle, who has a trailer for transporting the books from Queenie's house to the bookshop. I've got some time off on Friday, and Lionel and I have arranged to meet that morning at half past ten. Then on the games evening front, I managed to ring round the choir and arranged to collect from them every board game they could lay their hands on for Saturday night. At last, it seemed, we were getting somewhere.

After work I drove round to the choir members who'd offered the board games and picked them up, then spent the evening at Queenie's old house separating out potentially saleable stuff from what was clearly destined for the dustbin and therefore not worth bothering Fred with at all. It was a massively long job, as her collection was very large indeed. I still hadn't finished when her grandson arrived with a group of friends at around ten, and since I had no desire to be in the way I took the final three crates home with me so I could complete the task that evening. Queenie's reading tastes were certainly very catholic, embodying her love of music and her imaginative cookery which had served the choir so well over the years. But my two most interesting finds were not books at all. Firstly, I discovered a further assortment of board games which seemed to have a thinner layer of dust on them than Henry's collection; as one of the boxes actually had the manufacturers' website details on it, I guessed there was a good chance that at least some of them had last seen the light of day this side of the relief of Mafeking. I had no hesitation in requisitioning them for Saturday. Secondly, I found a whole carrier bag of music that she'd obviously taken home to look at during her choir membership but had never got round to returning. Since I noticed at once that some of it was music that Tripplehorn had demanded to have returned forthwith "on pain of summary execution by my own personal hit squad" I felt it was the least I could do to call him and tell him that I'd located it.

"Well, fancy that," he said with a chuckle. "Do you know, it never occurred to me that Queenie might have it. I guessed it was Kelvin Throckleby. You may remember him. Was in the choir just before you joined, then disappeared. I think he thought he'd got the music and had lost it. I've often wondered where he went."

"I take it you'd like me to bring it straight round to you?" I asked him.

"Oh, heavens, no," he replied. "We've only just got rid of one load of rubbish. Use it to stock up the church hall washrooms until the PCC get round to debating whether they can afford to buy another roll."

Which may prove an easier assignment than tracking down Kelvin Throckleby among the more remote outposts of the Gobi Desert and advising him that he may discard his camouflage gear, steel helmet, bullet-proof vest and round-the-clock police protection.

Friday 24th January

Lionel arrived at my house just as the phone rang. It was Henry Peasgood telling me that there'd been a slight hitch as far as his surprise item was concerned, and would I mind awfully if that particular aspect of the evening was cancelled. Whilst I was reassuring him that it was awfully good of him to ring and I quite understood and there was really no need to worry, at the same time punching the sky in unbridled ecstasy, Lionel enterprisingly took it upon himself to load on to the trailer the bags full of books I'd had to sort at home. Since he had already loaded the books I'd left at Queenie's, we were able to go straight on into the centre of town.

It was only as we pulled away from the traffic lights at the corner of Bradwell Road that I happened to glance back and saw that the trailer had far more material in it than I remembered packing up for Fred Robinson. A ghastly thought suddenly struck me, and a closer look through the rear windscreen confirmed the worst: as well as the books, we were also carrying all the board games which Lionel had for reasons best known to himself picked up with the books and added to the trailer. They had been wrapped in three large but very flimsy carrier bags. Before I had the chance to get Lionel to stop the car, I saw the bags suddenly topple off the trailer and into the path of a Mazda coming the other way. The driver of the car instinctively swerved to avoid it, and his front offside collided with the front offside of a Vauxhall travelling immediately behind us; both cars ground to a halt; and the van and the bus travelling behind the Mazda and the Vauxhall respectively failed to stop in time and ploughed into the vehicles in front of them, triggering a succession of further shunts in their wake.

Of course, it all happened so quickly. It may have been seen differently by the bemused bystanders, the police who attended at the scene and reported Lionel for carrying an insecure load on his trailer, contrary to Section 40A of the Road Traffic Act 1988, the enraged van driver who suggested an altogether swifter method of dispensation of justice, and the local radio station which only three hours later was able to report the reopening of the road by which time all through traffic was gridlocked within a radius of fifteen miles.

Fred Robinson was most understanding when I rang him to explain that owing to the need to take Lionel home and calm him down over a cup of tea and a bowlful of Valiums, I would have to come back with the books another day. "Dear Lionel," he said. "Not the brightest star in the sky. Bit like his cousin, bless her. You may know her. Joan Trumpington."

I asked him why on earth he'd recommended him, knowing what he did about the pair of them.

"Oh," he said, "Joan's one of my best customers. She orders all her books from me and pays in advance. She never asks for her money back if I can't find them."

I somehow managed to drag myself to choir tonight and endeavoured to drum up support for the games evening, not that the seizure of the bags of games by the police will have helped my cause in the slightest. The only definite yes I had at the end of the evening was Arthur Ramsbottom who promised to bring his friend Enid Hepplewhite, explaining that although at eighteen and a half stone she might struggle with squash or pole vaulting, she played a fairly mean game of tiddlywinks. I didn't like to discourage him by saying that none of these respective pursuits were in fact planned for Saturday, especially having regard to the response, or lack of it, of his colleagues in the choir. One could readily understand Eileen's inability to attend, owing to her having booked tickets months ago for the LSO at the Albert Hall. One was entitled to be less convinced altogether by Irving Cattermole's claim to have won a luxury week's windsurfing on the Humber Estuary.

Saturday 25th January

Rang Katie hoping that she might have some board games to offer for tonight, but the only thing she recalled that she possessed in that line was a pack of playing cards.

"They were given to me by one of my ex-boyfriends as a Valentine present," she explained.

"Terrific," I said, "just the job for tonight."

"Not with the pictures on the back of them, they won't be," she replied.

We decided to meet up in town and raid the charity shops, managing between us to obtain a draughts set, a chess set, a snakes and ladders game and Cluedo. Which was fine until we subsequently discovered that a bishop and two pawns were missing from the chess set, the snakes on the snakes and ladders game had been adorned with symbols and annotations which made Katie's pack of pornographic playing cards seem positively tasteful, and both Reverend Green and Colonel Mustard had absconded from the Cluedo house taking with them the elephant gun and wiping the billiard room from the face of the earth.

The result was that the ten punters were left with the choice between backgammon, snooker, table tennis and draughts. Henry Peasgood and one of his nephews got down to a game of draughts which judging by the grim expressions on their faces and the time they were taking on their moves looked set to last the whole evening; none of the remaining eight had ever played, nor were willing to learn, backgammon or snooker. And since we'd decided to ask for payment per game, rather than for the whole evening, the remaining alternatives of table tennis, table tennis and table tennis were clearly hopelessly unprofitable. I did at least persuade the eight attenders to pay to take part in a knockout, but it would have been churlish not to have refunded their entry fees to them when Enid Hepplewhite trod on the only ping-pong ball available, lost her balance,

lurched forward into the table and caused it to crash majestically to the floor.

It would in some ways have been easier to cope with had it not been match point in the final. And had she actually been one of the players.

"Don't worry," said Arthur Ramsbottom as, thanks to the combined brute force of the more muscle-bound competitors, Enid was hoisted back on to her feet while the table made a somewhat undignified exit stage left. "I've got something in lieu of Henry's surprise item. I think it'll amuse you."

I doubted that very much indeed, and my anxieties were not assuaged in the slightest when I saw him reach into his Superdrug carrier bag and produce a video cassette. He then announced that those present this evening were privileged indeed, for they would be witnesses to the first public showing of a piece of film of the St Basil's choir that he believed had been wiped from the archive. The October 1990 evensong at the church of Our Lady Of Sorrows, Datchet, preceded by picnic lunch and the mysterious disappearance of Luke Pimblett's tongue sandwiches.

Perhaps it was just as well that courtesy of the ample refreshment kindly provided by Steve combined with the exertions of the knockout contest and the unscheduled wrestling matches with an aged table tennis table and an even more aged Enid Hepplewhite, snores were emanating from the majority of the assembled company long before the involvement of the Special Branch.

Sunday 26ᵗʰ January

Needless to say, I wasn't at my brightest for this morning's service. The choice of hymns was uninspired and the congregational mass setting was equally gloomy. The composer had rather unwisely provided for a long held note on the word "peace" at the very end of the Agnus Dei, obviously not allowing for the lack of breath control of members of both the choir and congregation, and the resultant hissing sound created by those present gave the impression less of an act of worship than a snake charmers' convention. What made it more of a pity was that Katie was in the congregation; she's already thinking about signing up for confirmation classes, and the last thing I want to do is put her off at this early stage. She tactfully said nothing about the adder impersonations when we met up after the service, but on the musical side generally she told me she had a suggestion to make.

"Why don't you organise a Favourite Hymns evening," she said. "Everyone writes down on a bit of paper a hymn they like to sing, they put it in an envelope with a pledge of some money for the vestry, and then you put them all together and perform them."

The more I thought about the idea, the more I liked it. There are so many great hymns, and besides the classic favourites, there are several that are particularly apposite for members of the congregation. Mr Sprackley, the optician, would enjoy *Christian Dost Thou See Them*; Commander Wright, *Soldiers Of Christ Arise*; Rose Haughtrey, the baker's wife, *I Am The Bread Of Life;* Ian German, a retired meteorologist, *Hail The Day That Sees Him Rise*; James Cartlcdge, a Beatles fan, *Take My Life And Let It Be*; Alan Davies, who's a financial adviser with a Middle Eastern company, *On Jordan's Bank The Baptist Cry*; and for poor old Mike Summerfield, who's going through a messy divorce, *Fight The Good Fight With All Thy Might*. And if we wanted to serenade our ageing Bishop, who hasn't visited St Basil's for nearly twelve years, we could always rattle off *Immortal Invisible*.

Tuesday 28th January

I sat at home tonight feeling quite despondent, facing the prospect of reaching the end of January without having raised a single penny for the vestry appeal. The books are now with Fred Robinson and he tells me he'll have a price for them in a fortnight, but he's advised me not to be too optimistic of a large sum. And the contributions made by the two draughts players on Saturday, the only money we'd actually collected from the games evening, had just about covered the cost of a bottle of wine to thank Steve for the use of the house.

Arthur Ramsbottom phoned as I was putting my dinner in the microwave. He told me he's finished chapter two of the book, and is sticking rigorously to the word limits I've set. His main reason for calling, however, was to tell me he has details of a printing firm, Combiprint, who will bind and print books simply from material provided on disk, at amazingly competitive prices regardless of the size of the print run. He assured me that two friends of his used them quite recently and were very well satisfied with both the cost and the quality of the work.

Filled with fresh optimism and hope for the future, I dialled the number Arthur had given me and asked the man who answered if he would put me through to the manager of Combiprint.

"That was me," he replied, "until I sold the firm two years ago."

I asked him where the new owner might be located.

"Last thing I heard, fitting gas boilers in the Solomon Islands," he said.

Friday 31st January

Well, perhaps things are looking up. Tonight at rehearsal we agreed a date for two functions in aid of the vestry fund. The first will be a car boot sale on February 22nd, and the second will be a Favourite Hymns evening, as Katie had suggested, to take place on March 9th subject to clearance from Cora Willoughby-Smith who's just taken on the job of church bookings supervisor. Cora was away tonight and therefore couldn't confirm the date.

The Favourite Hymns evening was, however, not arranged without a degree of resistance from Tripplehorn. "If you think I'm going to give up my Sunday evening to play *Dear Lord And Father Of Mankind* and *How Great Thou Art* however many times they're requested, you're sadly mistaken," he said bluntly. "*Amazing Grace, Sing Hosanna* and *Jerusalem* are out, so is any Taize chant, anything included in *Hymns For The Modern Church*, anything which the congregation might be tempted to clap along with, and if we must have *At The Name Of Jesus* I'm not playing that ghastly modern tune."

Wondering how many hymns that would actually leave us with, I said we would obviously do our best to see that his wishes were respected.

"Oh, and one other thing," he said as we were packing up at the end, "No more than three verses of any hymn. The more two-verse hymns you can find, the better."

He was still moaning about it in the pub afterwards, and laying down yet further ground rules. I think we'll be lucky if the evening ends up consisting of any more than the first verse of the National Anthem.

FEBRUARY

Sunday 2nd February – *CANDLEMAS*

There was excellent news this morning, as I heard that Steve has secured more work in the area and he's going to be with us for another couple of months at least. I always enjoy the liturgy and the music for Candlemas and I felt this morning's service was one of the nicest for a long time. Hazel Ledworthy did the intercessions and prayed for a "new sense of loving tolerance, gentleness and understanding between all brothers and sisters in Christ" – qualities that seemed somewhat lacking when I heard her yelling at Steve in the vestry afterwards for having had the temerity to place his choir robe on her personal coathanger. Cora Willoughby-Smith was another on whom Hazel's intercessions appeared to have had less than immediate impact. She advised me that the 9th March was quite out of the question for the Favourite Hymns evening as it would clash with a WI function in the church at the same time. "In future," she said, "will you kindly consult with me before even thinking about holding a church function where church premises fall to be used." She then marched off to take Claude Hensby to task for not consulting her about the churchyard working party on 12th July which clashes with the Combined Beavers and Brownies Sponsored Litter Picking Contest. I suppose it's an improvement on the standards of efficiency of the previous bookings supervisor, Daphne Hackforth, whose skill at triple-booking in the church had become legendary before her enforced confinement in Mapletrees, the town's twilight home for those with ongoing dementia. But at least with Daphne I wouldn't have walked away feeling as uncomfortable as an Aberdeen Angus on the down escalator at Cockfosters.

I managed to obtain a selection of alternative dates from choir members who were still around. Cora had gone by the time I'd finished, so phoned her later only to be told that none of the dates were any good. It was only after the most abject display of grovelling on my part, during which I'm sure I must have promised her everything from gala seats at the ENO's autumn production of *Rigoletto* to an all-expense-paid manicure at Madame de Roussillon's Luxury Beauty Parlour, Empire Square, Madras, that she condescended to ask Otis Snodgrass to bring forward his wedding rehearsal by thirty minutes, thereby freeing up the church for us from 7pm on the 16th March.

Annoyingly I was unable to ring round the choir to advise them because in the flurry of after-church activity this morning I'd left my choir directory in church. And doubtless to go inside the building to pick it up I will now need to submit an application form in triplicate, handwritten in black ink and block capitals, signed and witnessed by a commissioner for oaths or notary public, accompanied by two passport-sized photographs, the standard fee and three references from persons of good standing in the community, at least 14 days prior to the date of the visit in respect of which the application is made. Only too aware that the parking ticket I incurred in 1982 will probably disqualify me anyway.

Tuesday 4th February

Arthur Ramsbottom dropped some more of his script round tonight, and over tea I skimmed through it. One event he referred to was in spring 1928 when the choir revived the ancient Rogationtide tradition of "beating the bounds." He'd not elaborated on it so I rang him up to find out what this particular tradition was all about.

"Oh, it was quite an event," he replied. "The choir would walk round the entire parish boundary, singing hymns and anthems as they went. It was if you like a way of marking out their own territory and offering worship to God outside the walls of their own church."

It set me thinking that this year we could organise a similar event, involving the choir walking between churches and singing perhaps a matins at one church, lunchtime recital at the second and evensong or an evening concert at the third. We could raise money not only through collections at the time but sponsorship for successful completion of the walk.

It'll have to be properly organised and mapped out, of course, to avoid a repetition of the disasters of the last choir hike which took place eight or nine years ago. There again, Arthur's camcording of the event would have been almost watchable, even entertaining, had he managed to include Alison Burns attempting to walk through the slurry-infested quagmire at the bottom of Mudtruckle Lane in 4-inch heels, Cora Willoughby-Smith being stung by a wasp as she endeavoured to entertain her picnic companions with extracts from *Chu Chin Chow*, and Davina Prendergast, trapped in Piggery Field by Bronco the bull, endeavouring to fend off his voracious attentions with an oil-stained picnic rug and handfuls of cheese and onion Wotsits.

Friday 7th February

Margaret Pardew phoned me at work today to tell me her choice of hymn for the Favourite Hymns evening. "I've actually got two," she said. "*I Will Sing This Song For All Eternity* and *Lord Will You Be The Apple Of My Eye*. I learnt them at last month's Christian Winter Warmer Weekend at St Bede's House."

Somehow I can't see them surviving Tripplehorn's robust screening process and I was about to advise her not to share her choice with him at this stage, especially as he appears still to be having difficulty with the whole Favourite Hymns concept. But she went on to what I suspect was the real reason for her call, namely to share with me the latest list of appalling misfortunes that have been heaped upon her sister. In the last three months, apparently, her relationship with her boyfriend has broken up, she's found she's asthmatic, her contract with Wildbloods is not being extended beyond the end of March, and her dog has got distemper. "And," she said, "this morning at breakfast she broke one of my mum's precious vases."

"I didn't know she was living with your mum again," I said. "When did she move back?"

"On Christmas Day," Margaret replied, "when the roof of her top floor flat fell in."

Because Margaret will talk at seemingly endless lengths about her family problems if given the slightest encouragement, I felt it best to steer the conversation round to more cheerful topics, and asked her a bit more about the Winter Warmer Weekend. She told me that part of the weekend had been devoted to a workshop with a Christian musician and composer of national repute, and this set me thinking that we as a choir could try something similar for the vestry fund. We would all pay a contribution and have either a half day or full day of tuition and singing under the guidance of an expert.

Unfortunately tonight's practice was not a good time to mention it. Tripplehorn was in a quite vile mood and lost his temper three or four times. It was thus with incredulity that I saw Margaret go up to him afterwards and ask him if he would agree to play the two hymns she'd mentioned to me on the phone earlier. He drew in his breath sharply and said to her "Yes, by all means. That is, if you want to empty the church faster than an invading horde of hyenas on heat." Whereupon she burst into tears and ran out. I actually thought she came off remarkably lightly. I was already preparing to ward off an attack of well chewed HB pencils and low-flying copies of Volume Three of the Bumper Collection Of Easy Anthems.

Sunday 9th February

The vicar gave a good plug for both the Favourite Hymns evening and the car boot sale, both in aid of the vestry fund, at church this morning. Regarding the car boot sale, everyone is invited to bring along a car with things to sell, while we as choir members oversee the practical arrangements. The field is big enough to hold sixty cars at least, and already a good thirty car owners have signed up. "Now, of course," the vicar said, "we must just pray for some fine weather and trust the Lord to provide it!" There was a certain diffidence about the way those words were uttered which gave rise to some doubt in my mind as to whether the vicar actually meant it.

As we disrobed at the end, Irving Cattermole, who has agreed to support the car boot sale under some protest, came up to me and said "Shame I got my prayer in first. For ten inches of snow and hurricane force northerly winds." And he certainly sounded as if he did mean it.

Friday 14th February

With a day off today and Katie at work, I decided to do a preliminary planning exercise for the choir hike, choosing an area of fine countryside about an hour's drive from town with three or four churches within a reasonable radius. I got down to business straight away, heading for the first church on my list, St Saviour's at Everard-cum-Millicent. Despite the gloomy weather, I made intelligent use of my map to follow and, more importantly, note down paths that I hoped we would be using between the churches in a few months. I was beginning to enjoy the walk when, contrary to what my map appeared to suggest, a track that I was on petered out unexpectedly at the edge of a field full of cows with access to the field obstructed by a securely padlocked gate. Assuming that the gate had either been padlocked erroneously, or a farmer had had enough of ramblers crossing his land, I climbed over it, slipping as I did so and falling head first into an alarmingly fresh cow pat.

If I thought that things could only get better from me once I had first extricated my face from the heap of bovine deposit, and then fought my way through a herd of cattle whose inquisitiveness was surely a match for even the most hardened tabloid gossip columnists, I was sadly mistaken. The only way I could exit the field on the other side was by means of a barbed wire fence which not only tore my hitherto trusty walking trousers to ribbons but served to increase my doubts as to the accuracy of the map makers. By the time I'd clambered through a thicket of brambles that would have tested the endurance skills of a crack army patrol unit, been chased through a pool of manure adjoining rundown farm buildings by a pair of Dobermans, waded across a stream so deep that the water went up to my waist, been yelled at by a bearded tractor driver as I blundered my way through the edge of a ploughed field where even the firmer-looking furrows boasted the texture of watery chocolate blancmange, and been forced through the back garden of a private house in an attempt to be reunited with the road, I had to concede there was just a smidgeon of a chance that I might have lost my way.

Unfortunately, my exploits had not gone undetected. As I tried to climb the stone wall separating the garden from the road, a man I guessed to be in his sixties came out of the house and asked if I was lost. I approached him with some apprehension, expecting to be severely lectured on the laws of trespass and threatened with prosecution for criminal damage to a stone wall, ageing rose bush and fading rhubarb plant. I told him what I'd been doing, or at any rate attempting to do, and to my amazement he responded to my explanation not with a nonplussed frown but a warm smile. Shaking me by the hand, he told me he was Eric Littlejohn, churchwarden of St Saviour's, and he said that not only was he sure that the vicar would be delighted if our choir would sing there in the spring or early summer, but he, Eric, would be pleased to entertain us on his lawn afterwards. "Only come before the really hot weather kicks in," he said. "My prize blooms were absolutely wrecked by last summer's drought." And though horticulture is a subject about which I know next to nothing, I shortly found myself on the receiving end of a full description of every plant, flower and shrub in his garden, in which he took an obviously passionate interest.

By the time we'd had a cup of tea, I decided I didn't fancy any more walking and headed swiftly back into town, frankly not too worried that I hadn't got to see any of the churches I was supposed to have been viewing. Or that I'd completely forgotten to ask the name and phone number of the vicar of Eric's church. I was more concerned about which of his potentially prize-winning young plants had been squashed beneath my manure-stained right boot.

A shorter choir practice tonight as it was Valentine's night and several of the choir, myself included, had plans for later on. Steve was at the practice, and told us that if he was still around, he'd be pleased to join us for the Favourite Hymns evening. "If you can find a hymn that's suitable for a plumber, do let me know," he said with a laugh.

Brian pointed to what we'd been singing only a few minutes before and said "What about this: 'One deep calleth another because of the noise of the waterpipes!'" Even Tripplehorn found that very funny.

Only Henry Peasgood kept a straight face. "It's not actually a hymn, though, is it," he pointed out. "It's part of Psalm 42. Verse 9."

With his capacity to put a dampener on things, I think we've the perfect solution to the problem of Eric Littlejohn's withering hollyhocks.

Saturday 15th February

As Katie and I shopped in town this morning, an elderly lady came up to us and asked if I was a member of the St Basil's choir. Her face was vaguely familiar and I recognised her as someone who had been in church on Sunday. She announced herself as June Shuttleworth and told us that she was staying in the area with her brother for a few weeks. After kindly saying how much she'd enjoyed our singing she told me she'd heard the vicar mention the Favourite Hymns evening and said she'd be thrilled if we could sing the hymn *Jesus Speaks Above Life's Tempests*, to the tune Morris' 80th. She left her phone number with us and said if we could undertake to perform it, she would pledge a very substantial sum indeed. "I'll leave it with you," she said.

I was so desperate to get some money into the vestry fund that I spent a good hour and a half this afternoon trawling through every hymn book and chorus book in the vestry library but to no avail. I even rang up a couple of music shops and spent some time trying to find it on the Internet, with similar lack of success. Katie was less than impressed with my abandoning her for the afternoon and told me so, quite forcefully. Finally, as she threatened to see personally to it that I was the next to be struck down by one of the more ferocious of life's tempests, I had to admit defeat and rang June Shuttleworth with the sad news that we couldn't trace the hymn after all.

"Oh, I didn't think you would," she said. "It was written specially for me by my grandfather when I was nine. I don't think it was ever published, but you never know."

I asked her if she still had a copy. She replied that she had lost it about fifty years ago but could still remember most of the words of verses 1 and 7 and three or four lines of the tune. "Although it could have been eight lines," she conceded.

I asked her if she'd like to sing what she could remember on the basis that that might constitute some sort of a start. The ensuing warbling sounded less like a snatch of hymn than the noise I'd heard on my phone line two years ago when I found myself inadvertently connected to a fax machine in Sao Paolo. I thanked her and hung up, resigned firstly to missing out on June's donation and secondly to a necessarily expensive evening out with Katie by way of compensation for a completely wasted afternoon. I decided there and then that any hymn suggested to us for inclusion in the Favourite Hymns evening but unknown to Tripplehorn and myself would be rejected out of hand.

All the same, I couldn't help continuing to wonder if Morris' 80th alluded to the age of Mr Morris when he wrote it. Or the fact that this was his eightieth attempt at getting it right.

Sunday 16th February

A large congregation this morning which included Lord Buttermere. A keen music lover, Lord Buttermere still writes occasionally for music magazines. I only hoped that I was hallucinating when I thought I saw him scribbling in a notebook during our annual murdering of Wood's *O Thou The Central Orb*. I wasn't aware that any of the journals to which he contributed carried a Worst Parish Choir Of The Year contest.

All became clear when Tripplehorn came up to me afterwards and produced a note that had been handed to him by Lord Buttermere as he was leaving. The gist of the note was that His Lordship was looking forward to attending the car boot sale, and although unable to attend the Favourite Hymns evening, he would give generously to the vestry appeal if we sang his favourite hymn, *He Who Would Valiant Be*, on the night.

"Good news," said Tripplehorn. "Now for goodness sake don't do anything to upset him. Until we get the money anyway. You know how awkward he can be."

My confidence boosted by this development, I spent some time on the phone tonight with the owner of the field we're using for the car boot sale, agreeing start and finish times and means of access. He was extremely helpful and even wished us all the very best for a successful event. He then added "I just hope for your sake the weather stays fine!"

I assured him that most car-booters I know are very stoical, and find all manner of ways to keep their pitches dry.

"I don't mean that," he said. "I mean that field gets like a mudbath after a five-minute shower."

Seriously worried, I decided to seek reassurance by means of the telephoned premium-rate 7-day weather forecast advertised in our local directory. There was certainly enough padding and extraneous information to satisfy even the most avid weather watcher, as well as add a sizeable sum to his quarterly phone bill. However, the prognosis for the weekend seemed fairly vague, and I replaced the receiver quite unsure as to whether to expect balmy springlike sunshine or Arctic-borne blizzards. On the other hand I now consider myself an expert on the effect of the recent snowfalls on skiing prospects in the French Alps. Not to mention the freak heatwave currently affecting the Dolomites.

Thursday 20th February

The telephoned 7-day weather forecast promised excellent skiing conditions throughout the Alps but outbreaks of rain and strong winds for all parts of Britain by Saturday. Unfortunately this opinion appears to be shared by all other agencies whose forecasts I sought. From Suzie Bannister's Wizard Weekend Weather Watch in the local radio station lunchtime show to my work colleague Trevor Dawson and his piece of Herne Bay seaweed.

Friday 21st February

A slightly different forecast from Brioni Cartwright's Met Office Microscope in the local radio station breakfast show. It's not going to be "outbreaks of rain." It's going to be "continuous heavy rain." Meanwhile, conditions in the Alps have never been better. I was besieged by calls this evening asking if the car boot sale was still happening, and I patiently told them that yes, it was, unless conditions on the morning meant that it was physically impossible to continue with it. When at seven twenty tonight, just as I was about to go out to choir, the phone rang for the fourteenth or maybe the fifteenth time, and I was asked by the gruff male caller if he should still be coming in the morning I lost my patience and told him "Well, actually I'm in the process of transferring the whole event to the lower slopes of the Matterhorn, and turning it into a chairlift sale instead." He didn't sound too pleased.

I was in no mood to enjoy choir tonight and, to make matters worse, even those choir members who had promised their unstinting support were beginning to waver. Tripplehorn didn't give me one iota of encouragement and, as we rehearsed Psalm 148, he even had to have a cheap joke at my expense, making us sing the verse with the words "Fire and hail, snow and vapours; wind and storm fulfilling his word" at least five times. As we were packing up, he turned to me and asked me "Said your prayers for fine weather for the car boot sale for tomorrow?" I glanced across at Irving Cattermole, who looked a good deal too smug for my liking, and said "I think the prayers for the fire, hail, snow and vapours have had the first look-in, I'm afraid."

I saw Margaret looking quite upset and during coffee afterwards I apologised if I'd offended her.

"I think the trouble with our secular culture is that we don't place enough faith in God's ability to answer prayer," she said.

Irving Cattermole grinned at her and said "I don't know. I'm quite confident He'll answer mine" which made her even more agitated. Twenty minutes later the two of them were engaged in bitter argument, he stubborn and caustic, she angry and tearful. I'd no idea that a single car boot sale could form the basis of a whole theological debate.

Saturday 22nd February

Woke up at half past five and looked out of my bedroom window at a magnificent moon and a starlit sky. As I lay back down in my bed, I really started to believe in miracles.

By half past eight, it was bucketing with rain and blowing a gale, and by nine o'clock I'd already taken twelve calls from car owners cancelling their bookings. Presumably many more were trying unsuccessfully to get through to me, for I arrived at the field at nine thirty on foot to be greeted with the sight of just three vehicles, and even the drivers of those showed precious little inclination to get out and set up. As I arrived, Matthew Sparkes and a companion of roughly his age, whom he introduced to me as Tom, emerged from one of the vehicles and volunteered to navigate the cars into spaces. Their first assignment soon appeared in the form of Lord Buttermere who arrived in his large estate car and thanks to Matthew's navigational skills was thirty seconds later reversing it straight into the side of Delia Ponsonby's Mitsubishi Colt.

With names and addresses duly exchanged, Lord Buttermere, after taking me to task for my ill-chosen words on the subject of chairlift sales on the phone last night, lost little time in setting up his own weatherproof pitch consisting of windbreak and tarpaulins supported by sturdy wooden poles protecting a line of folding wooden tables. It truly was a work of art, and he must have been quite disappointed that only four people had deigned to inspect the goods he had on display before at around eleven twenty a particularly strong gust of wind lifted the windbreak and tarpaulins high into the air causing the poles, tables and unsold merchandise to crumple into a heap. Any thoughts of reassembling the pitch were sadly dashed when Matthew helpfully navigated the arriving vicar's car straight over the tarpaulin, leaving half the tarpaulin ripped to shreds and the other half tangled up in the vicar's exhaust system. By now Matthew's mum, who seemed to have spent all morning sitting in the car with her newspaper, clearly decided she'd had enough and started the car. But by this time the state of the ground rendered any forward or indeed backward progress impossible without assistance and, at my request, Lord Buttermere broke off from salvaging what remained of his potted geraniums and porcelain figurines to provide an encouraging push. For a few seconds the car remained rooted to the spot, then unexpectedly shot forward so fast that Lord Buttermere took an unscheduled dive into unquestionably the muddiest patch of the entire field.

I somehow doubt that the £4.73 we took this morning will go far towards the cost of replacing Lord Buttermere's rear bumper, tarpaulins and Savile Row windcheater. To say nothing of the Summer Holidays Afloat colour supplement in Alison's *Daily Mail* which had to be used to wipe the traces of dog dirt from his left knee cap.

Sunday 23rd February

A glorious sunny morning. I lost count of the number of people at church who told me the car boot sale should have been today, although how they could expect me to have been able to predict the weather three weeks ahead I cannot think. I could hardly bring myself to join in this morning's enthusiastic praises of fire, hail, snow, vapours etc. Afterwards Tripplehorn, who needless to say had not turned up himself yesterday, came up to me and, far from offering words of sympathy, merely said "Just as long as you didn't upset Lord Buttermere. His support certainly won't do our funds any harm."

I can think of one or two things that wouldn't do our choirmaster any harm. Like a good kick up the Dolomites.

Tuesday 25th February

With the car boot sale behind us, thoughts turned to the choir hike again. It was disappointing that Eric Littlejohn, on whom I was relying for details of the vicar of his church, appeared to be ex-directory, and Directory Enquiries were no help at all. Accordingly, I decided to use my day off today to have another try at the walk I had messed up so spectacularly ten days ago, and get the relevant details in the course of my explorations. Having quickly found where I'd gone wrong last time, I enjoyed an effortless and very pleasant walk through delightful scenery, and although my travels this time did not take me past Eric's, the board outside St Saviour's gave a choice of two phone numbers for the vicar. Using my mobile, I decided to phone him from there, and dialled the first number. The phone was answered almost at once by a man with an Asian accent. When I asked if I was speaking with the vicar, his reply was a puzzled "I beg your pardon?"

"That is the vicarage, isn't it?" I asked.

"No," he answered. "This is the Everard Tandoori."

I moved hastily on to the other number I had written down. This time it took ages firstly to get the ringing tone and secondly for anybody to pick up the phone. At length it was answered, by a man who sounded remarkably like the one I'd been speaking to a moment or so before.

"Can you tell me if the vicar's in, please," I said.

"Certainly I sell you chicken," the man replied. "How you like it – curry, tandoori, with chips?"

An hour and numerous phone calls later, I was still no nearer finding the vicar. But the tikka masala was delicious.

Thursday 27th February

Following a visit to the library at lunchtime, I did ascertain the correct office number of the vicar of Everard-cum-Millicent. He was most apologetic about my difficulties on Tuesday, explaining that the parish office had been relocated and the number had changed a year ago.

I told him that perhaps it was time the signboards outside the churches needed to be updated.

"Oh, that's down to Crispin Peacock," he said, "who has about as much organising ability as a porcupine on roller skates."

The vicar was a delightful man; he told me that he was in fact the vicar of all three churches I had in mind for us to visit, and seemed agreeable in principle to our visiting his churches to sing. He did however advise me I'd need to confirm precise dates and times with the man who dealt with the church bookings.

"And who is that?" I enquired.

"Crispin Peacock," said the vicar.

Having jotted down Mr Peacock's number I dialled it, and found myself seconds later in earnest conversation with the West Shires Massage And Waxing Clinic. But then, it wouldn't have surprised me at that particular moment if I'd been put through to the president of the West Of England Federation Of Roller-Skating Porcupines.

Friday 28th February

Fred Robinson rang this morning with a price for Queenie's books. It was rather more than I anticipated. Before I could get too excited, however, he went on to tell me that Lionel Harbottle has now a big bill from his insurers, representing the excess on his policy, in the wake of the claims following last month's accident. I feel I've no alternative but to pass Fred Robinson's cheque straight on to Lionel.

Rachel Ellis had a great idea at choir tonight. "Lent starts next week," she said, "so how would it be if we all got our friends and colleagues to sponsor us to give up something for Lent, or, better still, to achieve something like a weight loss, and give the money to the vestry fund."

There were one or two murmurs of approval, but whether or not there will be any take-up it's impossible to say. There is in fact ample scope for self-improvement within the choir ranks. Matthew could stop sucking sweets during the practices and then, on being told by his mother or Tripplehorn to desist, welding the unconsumed remains to the seats. Tripplehorn could curb his language which has been colourful to say the least over recent weeks. Hazel Ledworthy could stop scowling every time Tripplehorn announces we're to do a piece we've performed any less than 271 times before. Arthur Ramsbottom could be persuaded to sing perhaps one piece per service in tune and less than double forte. Henry Peasgood could stop name-dropping. Cora Willoughby-Smith could refrain from inventing her own descants to the last verse of the last hymn. Craig Dumbleton could try getting through a whole practice without reference to railways and particular the personnel on north west Kent suburban lines. And Irving Cattermole could try rehearsing a whole Stanford anthem without announcing his opinion that a better piece could have been written by a colony of dyslexic Latvian dung beetles.

There was some good news tonight. It seems that not only is the hire charge for the field for the car boot sale being waived because of the weather, but Lord Buttermere has said he can claim for the damaged bumper off his insurance, the tarpaulins had been loaned from a friend who died last month, and he was going to throw out his windcheater anyway. Thereby enabling us to end the month £4.73 in profit. Which when the vestry work starts should be just enough to cover the workmen's bacon butties for the first morning.

That is, if they agree to go without brown sauce.

Sunday 2nd March

Following a renewed plea by the vicar this morning, suggestions for hymns for the 16th were pouring in. Lucy Maybury, aged seven, came up to me after the service and asked if we could sing the hymn about Brighton. I confessed to her that although I did not for a moment doubt that there were many aspects of Brighton that were worthy of Christian praise, I couldn't immediately think of any hymn writers who have thought to express them in words and music. I suppose I could have suggested *O Jesus I Have **Prom**ised, **Rock** Of Ages Cleft For Me, Guide Me O Thou Great Je**hove**ah, Christ Whose Glory Fills The Skies* with its line "Daystar in my heart ap**pear**"(pier), or indeed the line from *O Worship The King*, namely "**Pavilion**ed in splendour and girded with praise," but the connection between these hymns and the South coast resort struck me as a little too esoteric. It was only over lunch when Katie pointed out to me that what Lucy was actually requesting was *All Things Bright And Beautiful.* And that I could hardly criticise, having confessed to her that I'd once come home from school having sung *Lord Of The Dance* and asked my mum what a "dance settee" was.

Ash Wednesday 5th March

A tiring day at work and quite a long service tonight with a thought-provoking sermon about the need to mortify our bodily lusts before the Lord and to become dynamic instruments of godly love in an increasingly self-indulgent world. I suspect that what the preacher had in mind went rather beyond the Lenten sacrifices to which I'd already mentally subscribed, namely twenty press-ups every morning and only plain Hobnobs with my coffee after choir practice. But after the service, Tripplehorn provided some unexpected inspiration for a somewhat deeper level of seasonal commitment. "I've just been talking to Anthony Cartwright," he said. "As you know, he's one of our wealthier parishioners. There's a substantial sum available from a trust fund set up by his late father to provide for the furtherance of the musical traditions of St Basil's, and the raising of the profile of our music beyond the four walls of our church. He's inviting entrants for a competition to compose the anthem for the choir to premiere at Evensong on Pentecost Sunday at Exeter. The winner will get a big cash prize, and the choir will get an even larger sum when the anthem's performed at Exeter. Anyone can enter, not just St Basil's members, but it would obviously be great if one of us were to submit the winning anthem. The closing date is Good Friday." As he spoke, he did seem to be looking in my direction, perhaps mindful of the Harvest anthem I'd composed last year but which had never been performed.

On the way home, I told Katie about it. She was quite unequivocal. "Go for it," she said. "If you win, and there's no reason why you shouldn't, you could donate at least part of the prize to the vestry fund. And the choir donation could go to the fund as well."

Although it was late by the time she'd gone home, I couldn't resist digging out my music manuscript paper and making a start. The first challenge was the title. *Come Holy Spirit* is a bit predictable and I'm sure it's been used before. I was tempted to go for something dramatic and slightly mysterious and had in mind *The Wind From Afar,* only then realising that the addition of a single letter to the title on pre-performance publicity by Matthew or one of his waggish cronies would expose my work to ridicule. Finally, after much deliberation, I decided on *Spirit Of Fire*: punchy, dramatic and eye-catching. I thought I should at least try and get down the first line of music before turning in for the night, but a combination of composer's block, heavy eyes and a rather good film on one of the Sky movie channels forced me to give up the struggle after a couple of bars.

But at least with this project, for which I've set aside all of Lent, I can now say I've a clear focus for both spiritual development and mortification of the baser bodily impulses that would otherwise obstruct my path to perfect union with Christ. And can get back on the chocolate Hobnobs.

Friday 7th March

We have a new choir member. Her name is Ruth Hartnell. Although her best singing years are, on her own admission, behind her, she still feels she has a lot to offer the choir of St Basil's. Apparently she was in the choir of a nearby village church which has now disbanded owing to the fact that all the other sopranos in it have died. It wasn't long before she was making her presence felt among us in the most annoying way possible, querying the speed and dynamics of just about every piece we were singing. But at least she seemed reasonably switched on, and anybody who can reach right across Hazel Ledworthy and remove the choir eraser from beneath her packet of honey menthol Tunes without prompting armed guards to open immediate fire and let loose a pack of hungry Alsatian dogs is deserving of respect if not sheer admiration.

In fact, so bowled over was I by her no-nonsense attitude towards Hazel Ledworthy that over coffee I mentioned my fundraising activities to her, explaining that we had not got off to the most propitious start and asking if she might have a few ideas of her own.

"Of course," she said. "Come round to my house on Tuesday week at 7.45. The Old Bridge House, Marchwood Road. I'll run a couple of suggestions by you. Shouldn't take long."

In the pub afterwards I asked Ken Foulkes if he'd had dealings with her before.

"Our previous neighbour worked with her," he said. "Apparently she was sacked from her job because they found her too cold and impersonal."

"And what job was that?" I asked.

"Inland Revenue inspector," he replied.

I stayed on for some time over a surprisingly convivial brandy with Tripplehorn as well as Ken, Brian and Rachel this evening to talk over the Favourite Hymns programme. With at least twelve people selecting *Dear Lord And Father Of Mankind*, eleven choosing *How Great Thou Art* and ten plumping for *The Old Rugged Cross*, the number of hymns we might have had to sing is rather less than feared. We can also discount some other requests, including *The Holy City* (verdict: not a hymn), Number 943 in *Hymns For Today's American Church* (verdict: who do we know with a copy of the music and would we want it anyway) and "that nice one they used to do on *Stars On Sunday* starting "dah-dee dah-dee daaah-deeee"(verdict: Mavis Tinsley's back on the sherry again).

Sunday 9th March – *FIRST SUNDAY IN LENT*

A chance to contribute to another good cause today, as our church was organising a 12.30pm Hunger Lunch, the first of three such lunches on Sundays during Lent, with simple fare such as rolls, cheese and salads and all profits from the lunches going to our link parish in West Africa. Unfortunately Katie couldn't come but I decided I'd still like to go.

A suitably solemn service this morning. Joan Trumpington was the only choir member away. Afterwards Tripplehorn hurried up to me and told me he had a problem. "I'm desperate for a copy of the *Golden Bells* hymn book," he said. "Lady Patterson, who'll be good for a few bob next Sunday, has signed up for a hymn I know is only in that book. Joan swore blind she'd dropped a copy round to my house yesterday morning but I can't see where she left it. I rang her last night and she told me she's sure there's at least two in the music cupboard. Problem is, I'm due to play at St Wilfrid's in twenty minutes and I'm desperate to get to work on these hymns this afternoon. Could you possibly go through the music cupboard and when you've found the book can you kindly bring it round to me?"

It sounded a reasonable enough request. Until I began looking through the music cupboard and found scenes of chaos that made Monday morning on the North Circular during a snowstorm look positively regimented. In the end I was reduced to flinging virtually all the contents of the cupboard on to the vestry floor in order that I might have a sporting chance of seeing exactly what lay within. There were some surprising discoveries, from a letter addressed to Joan Trumpington dated 23rd August 1968, threatening legal proceedings for an unpaid invoice for four copies of Chetwynd Dibble's masterpiece *Bring Hither The Tabret* at two shillings and sixpence each plus postage and packing, to a comic which one assumes was confiscated from a mischievous treble and featuring such comfortably believable characters as the world-saving superhero Gondremarck the Magnificent and the evil Professor Primaface Potemkin with a scary propensity for surgical brain replacement. But, despite an extensive and lengthy search, of *Golden Bells* there was no sign.

It was half past one when I finally arrived at the church hall to find the last crumbs of bread and unwanted strands of lettuce being swept into the dustbins. I went home in a fury and rang Tripplehorn to tell him the bad news.

"Oh, there was no problem in the end," he said airily. "It turned out that Joan had delivered the book to the house next door by mistake. My neighbour came round with it an hour ago."

I told him that thanks to her incompetence, I had just missed the hunger lunch.

"Unless I've missed something, I thought the whole idea of a hunger lunch was to go hungry," he said. "You've gone hungry – what more could you ask?"

At that precise moment, a family-sized portion of roast beef and Yorkshire pudding. And for Professor Primaface Potemkin to be dragged out of semi-retirement to get to work on Joan Trumpington. Preferably on a no-win no-fee basis.

Friday 14th March

Another long chat with Margaret on the phone tonight. She sounded very down. She reminded me that nothing further has been said or done about her suggestion of a workshop day led by a well-established composer or conductor. "I would have mentioned it at tonight's practice," she said, "but I've a really bad cold and can't make it. Can you say something when you get the chance?"

With the Favourite Hymns evening preoccupying all of us just now, I said I might struggle to get such an opportunity. My response seemed to plunge her into even greater depths of despair and before long I was receiving the latest update on the various calamities to befall her this week, beginning with the untimely demise of Cecil the goldfish and ending with a blown gasket on the B3079 by the Happy Farm battery chicken coops. By way of cheering her up, I told her I'd try to incorporate some additional Christian input into the Favourite Hymns evening by suggesting to the vicar that some of those present might like to introduce their favourite hymn and tell the congregation why it meant so much to them. I was delighted to be able to ring her back a few minutes later and advise her that the vicar was wholly in agreement.

What should have been a most enjoyable practice rehearsing the hymns for Sunday evening was spoilt by the news that because a lot of photocopying needs doing for hymns that aren't in the normal books we will have to have an additional practice on Sunday afternoon to go through them once the copying has been done. By me, needless to say. The practice was made no more enjoyable by Ruth's insistence that we put markings against each verse to indicate whether we are to sing them in unison or harmony or whether we wish them to be soft, loud or somewhere in between. She also said that it would be a good idea for certain verses to be sung by women's voices only and others by men's, and before long we found ourselves with a whole range of different sexes and classes of people to sing verses of their own. With the two-verse *Let All The World In Every Corner Sing,* unison throughout, there was little room for confusion, but with the 7 – or was it 8 – verse *For All The Saints,* I suspect I wasn't the only one querying which verse was to be sung by the men, which by ladies over 37, which by members of the congregation with black shoes, and which by anybody with an inside leg measurement of less than 31 inches.

I could see that Lesley was looking exceedingly fed up. She held her tongue admirably until near the end when Ruth suggested that we have an allargando on the words "In England's green and pleasant land." At which point Lesley snapped "Is someone going to tell me what an allargando is?"

Unwisely Tripplehorn retorted "I'll tell you in the pub afterwards."

Why he couldn't have told her there and then I can't think. It would then have avoided a lengthy and noisy debate between Lesley and Rachel lasting most of the rest of the practice as to whether it was the latest make of Ford car or a venomous snake indigenous to the riverbanks of the Upper Volta. And of course Matthew couldn't resist offering a few suggestions of his own which were less than warmly received by Tripplehorn who summarily condemned him to the dressing rooms for his third early bath in nine months. Then again, there's no reason why it shouldn't have lent its name to a computer game or a new brand of cheese and celery potato snack.

Sunday 16th March

A last, a fundraising event that could be called a success.

During the morning service, the vicar made a final request for hymns and pledges for tonight – because of our extra afternoon rehearsal, Tripplehorn had agreed to accommodate some last-minute requests provided they were in one of the hymn books we already had – and also asked for volunteers to give personal testimonies. Tripplehorn, who apparently hadn't found out about the testimonies till this morning, wasn't best pleased. "I thought we'd got this malarkey down to an hour, tops," he said. "The last thing I want is a troop of octogenarians spouting about how their flagging faith was revitalised by their newsagent's second cousin's miraculous recovery from housemaid's knee." I somehow think that's us off the *Songs Of Praise* shortlist.

Despite the annoyance of the photocopying and the extra practice, I really enjoyed the evening and I think the large congregation did so too. In recognition of the large number of requests for *Dear Lord And Father Of Mankind,* we did it as an encore at the end as well as near the start; and despite Tripplehorn's earlier rather harsh views of what were acceptable hymns and what were not, we did Graham Kendrick's *The Servant King* and *Shine Jesus Shine* which are in my view two of the best modern hymns in regular use. Whatever the Tripplehorns and the Cattermoles of this world may say, there is some really great modern hymnody around and I guess more people will have gone away humming those two hymns, or Katie's choice *Morning Has Broken,* than some of the alleged gems of the past that we laboured through during the hour and a quarter that it lasted. It was great to have enjoyed the evening and also to feel that the vestry fund campaign had, at last, properly got off the ground.

Thanks to some discreet and obviously very delicate negotiation between Tripplehorn and the vicar – I'm sure I recognised a man who emerged from the vestry with them as a senior United Nations official who obviously found Middle East peacekeeping insufficiently challenging for him – the testimonies were kept short and snappy, with not a housemaid's knee in sight. One of those who gave a testimony was a visitor named Melvyn Samlesbury. He was tall, clean-cut and immaculately dressed, and at least a generation younger than most of tonight's congregation. He announced that he was a composer and conductor of various prize-winning choirs and orchestras in Lancashire. He was on holiday in the area for a week and had come along to St Basil's, in his words, "to road-test your Sunday morning worship." Hence his finding out about the Favourite Hymns evening and putting in a last-minute hymn request and offer of testimony. He struck me as an absolutely ideal person to lead a workshop day as Margaret had suggested.

I'd hoped to get together with both him and Tripplehorn afterwards to discuss it, but Tripplehorn had disappeared as soon as the singing was over so I decided to go and meet him on my own. Having prised him away from Lesley, who seemed very taken with him indeed, I got as much information about him as I could, including his website details, and provisionally arranged May 10th for him to join us for the day.

When I got home I logged straight on to Melvyn's website. Lesley will doubtless be delighted to glean, as I did, by clicking on "All About Me" that he is single and lives alone in a converted barn within sight of Pendle Hill with two cats and a rapacious budgerigar. Those who feel that church choir membership is for wimps could do worse than note from the same page that he has run summer schools on the subject of Persuasiveness Through Music in the new conference centre just outside Accrington. More discerning choir members may be reassured to learn, as any Internet user could by clicking on to the "Testamonials" (sic) page that the combined choirs of St James The Less and St Peter ad Vincula, North Burnley, were "thoroughly delighted with your reasonable rates and no-nonsense coaching which led us to unpredecented (sic) heights of musical ecstasy." But Tripplehorn, who proved unreachable for the rest of the evening, would not necessarily be impressed with the result of clicking on to the "Curculicum Vita"(sic) page. Which revealed that the "prize-winning" to which he alluded during his testimony appeared to be restricted to joint third prize four years ago, and joint fourth prize three years ago, for the Best Church Choir at the Music And Speech Festival organised by the Nelson and Clitheroe Miners' Welfare Institute.

Tuesday 18th March
My meeting with Ruth tonight. She'd invited Craig Dumbleton along as well for some reason, but even with him there I needn't have worried about it going on too long. She began by telling us she had one or two vague ideas but was certainly amenable to better suggestions and asked us if we had any.

"A special choir outing," suggested Craig.

"I don't think so," said Ruth.

"A summer fayre," Craig advocated.

"Not if I can help it," said Ruth.

"A sponsored 24-hour sing," Craig proposed.

"Over my dead body," said Ruth.

I bided my time while Craig came up with further possibilities, all of which received either brusque shakes of the head or frowns which if administered from the shores of Loch Ness would have frightened any monster lurking within its waters into remaining invisible for at least another four hundred years.

Eventually I decided to offer my contribution.

"A gala summer concert, perhaps at Cora's if she'll have us, featuring a mixture of choir items and guest professional musicians, with buffet supper plus raffle or auction of promises, perhaps late July," I began.

"Yes, that's an excellent idea," said Ruth.

"And then, near Christmas, a humorous one-act play in the church hall followed by seasonal refreshments then carols for choir and audience in the second half," I went on.

"Another excellent idea," beamed Ruth. "Meeting over. Thank you."

I felt as though I'd just got two questions right on *Brain Of Britain*. It was grand to know that my antennae were so much in tune with an obviously born organiser possessing such a combination of experience and single-mindedness.

Of course it helped that I was sitting next to her. And able to read from the list of events she'd made out before the meeting started.

Friday 21st March

Another day off today, which I had set aside purposely in order to do some serious work on *Spirit Of Fire*. I've so many things planned with Katie for the next few weeks, and risk making myself so unpopular if I back out of any of them, that a good day's graft on it today was absolutely essential. But as I awoke and set about the affairs of the day, I really did wonder if it was all worth it. I reckoned there was bound to be some quite fierce competition from far more experienced and competent musicians who only needed a couple of hours to rattle off a piece that would make mine look positively naff by comparison. So I rang Tripplehorn to ask how many other entries he was aware of.

"I'm not sure," he said, "but I know Mike Pitheavlis is having a go."

Mike Pitheavlis had played the organ for us one Sunday in Tripplehorn's absence last summer and, although he was known not to have much time for church music or indeed church anything, I knew him to be incredibly gifted musically. Relieved, I laid *Spirit Of Fire* aside.

Ruth Hartnell cornered me after choir tonight and talked me through her ideas on the two functions we had so democratically agreed she would organise, meaning that there was no chance to discuss with Tripplehorn the possibility of our inviting Melvyn Samlesbury. I went to the pub in the hope of catching him there instead, but there was no sign of him. Henry Peasgood was there, however, and as I know how au fait he is with church affairs, I asked him if he knew how many entrants there were for the competition.

"I don't know of any other entries besides Mike's," he said, "and I don't think Mike's too bothered about coming out on top. So if you've written anything, it's probably down to you or there'll be no entries at all."

With a sinking heart, I asked him why he considered Mike not to be excessively fussed about the result.

"It's something of an experimental piece he's written," Henry replied, "called *Sonata In F Flat Minor*. It includes a whoopee cushion going off, a firework exploding, squashed tomatoes being thrown at the audience, and a female member of the choir bashing the organ manual with her head and sticking out her bottom at the second basses."

"I see," I said, "and where does the Pentecost part come in?"

"I don't think he's planning to get round to that," said Henry.

Sunday 23rd March

Steve's last Sunday with us. I was really sorry to see him go and I think most of the rest of us were as well. We clubbed together to buy him a small gift and card which we presented to him after the service. He made a super little speech, telling us that if we needed any plumbing for our newly restored vestry, he would do it at a discount and "even throw in a khazi for free to walk round to the church hall." I saw Zoe approach him afterwards and I had this horrible feeling she was going to ask him what a khazi was. Fortunately she didn't. She in fact proceeded to tell him she was interested in pursuing a career in music and asked him if he had any advice. Steve was very good with her, giving her a number of suggestions about where to study and how she should continue with her musical education during the rest of her schooldays, and wishing her every success. She went away quite happily. As she did so Steve turned to me and said "Reminds me. What do you ask someone with a music degree?"

I told him I had no idea.

"'Can I have two quarter pounders and two large fries please?'" he replied.

As he was going I saw him embracing and kissing some of the ladies in the choir, Cora Willoughby-Smith and Ruth Hartnell included. For one surreal moment I thought I saw him about to make an attempt on Hazel Ledworthy, but one glance at her stern and unyielding south-west face, icy upper slopes and steely grey summit features caused him to make a prudent retreat at base camp.

His departure will certainly make it easier to restore flexibility to the seating arrangements, which have become somewhat unwieldy since Ruth Hartnell ceased to be on speaking terms with Cora, Ruth and Hazel. Bearing in mind Ruth has only been in the choir for sixteen days, this is no small achievement and I sought out the latest section of Arthur Ramsbottom's totally forgettable prose to see if anyone had topped it. Not wholly to my surprise, there was no mention of anything of the kind whatsoever. It was left to Ken Foulkes to give me the answer. "Prudence O'Leary," he said. "None of the choir were on speaking terms with her when she joined it."

It does strike me that we might have a chance of selling more than a single figure number of copies of his book for the vestry fund if a few more instances of major choir conflicts or indeed choir oddities generally had found their way into the text. The 1970 feud between Peregrine Hicks and Laetitia Molesworth-Bricket over the music stand polishing duty roster hardly qualifies as the choir battle of the century. As for choir oddities, I'm sure it can't take much research on Arthur's part to unearth more interesting facts than the one revealed on page 28. That in the last nine years alone, choir members have availed themselves of at least 14 different types of throat lozenge.

Friday 28th March

Thankfully, there was a suitable opportunity tonight to put to Tripplehorn and the choir the possibility of Melvyn Samlesbury coming to lead a workshop day in May, with choir members paying to take part and proceeds going to the vestry fund. It has to be said that waiting for Tripplehorn to be in the right mood for a proposal of this nature is rather like the position a cymbals player in an orchestra finds himself – miss the moment, and it's gone for ever – but tonight he seemed in an unusually agreeable frame of mind and when I made the suggestion that Melvyn Samlesbury join us for the day, he was really quite positive about the idea. Indeed he went so far as to say that he did remember him vaguely from a Royal School Of Church Music Combined Choirs Evensong a few years back, and although in Tripplehorn's words "he struck me as a couple of pieces of sticky-back plastic short of a Blue Peter badge," his overall impression of him was reasonably favourable.

"So I can go ahead and book him?" I asked.

"Yes, do," Tripplehorn replied, "but we shall all know who to blame if it goes pear-shaped."

As if this overwhelming vote of confidence in the likely success of the day were not enough, I then promptly found myself lumbered not only with handling the booking arrangements with Mr Samlesbury and negotiating a fee which is still going to leave us in profit on the day, but also taking delivery of any glittering examples of Mr Samlesbury's work that he thinks we ought to rehearse in advance.

Decided to leave directly after the rehearsal, go home and get on with it straight away. I approached the task with some apprehension, fully aware from Melvyn Samlesbury's website of his expertise in the art of persuasiveness. But Katie, who was staying overnight with me, told me not to worry. "Remember," she said as she stirred the tomato soup, "he's hardly a household name and it's not as if you're desperate to have him."

Which made it all the more inexplicable that ten minutes later I had not only agreed that we would undertake to copy all the music he was sending to us but had also accepted responsibility for half his petrol money and the cost of an overnight stay with full English breakfast in the Swan Hotel. It was perhaps fortunate that Katie was removing warm rolls from the oven and motioning me to sit down and get on with supper before his persuasiveness skills had charmed me into offering him, at our expense, a six-course dinner with champagne in L'Hirondelle in King Street followed by a ride in a chauffeur-driven Mercedes to Abbey Grove for a ninety-minute session in Mehmet Bin Soud's All Over Massage and Pedicure Parlour.

Mothering Sunday 30th March

A glorious sunny day. Katie had her parents staying with her for the weekend and they came along to the service this morning. Like her, they have never been churchgoers, but they seemed to enjoy the service very much. I felt quite emotional when during the singing of Rutter's *For The Beauty Of The Earth* Katie went up with many of the congregation to collect a little bunch of flowers for her mother. She told me afterwards that it was the first Mothering Sunday in her life that she had done this. I really felt a very strong sense of God working in us and through us. It was an exciting feeling and helped to make it, for me at least, a beautiful act of worship.

In the vestry afterwards, Tripplehorn circulated a list of weddings for the next year for which a choir was likely to be requested. Although I seem to be unavailable for almost all of them, I told him, I believed out of the earshot of the others, that I had in mind to suggest that a percentage of the fees be donated to the vestry fund. Tripplehorn not as enthusiastic as I would have liked. It may or may not be significant that with the exception of the wedding of Lucy Shrimpton, who is a reasonably regular attender at St Basil's, none of the names on the list meant anything to us at all. Indeed Alison asked why, even with the promise of remuneration at the end of it, we should give up our Saturday afternoons for couples that we've never seen before and are unlikely to see again.

Margaret came up with an opposing view. "We talked about this at our Lent group meeting the other night," she said. "My friend Jamie made a very valid point which is that they are asking God to bless their union and it's not for us to judge their motives or their commitment. God will do that. As regulars at St Basil's we are charged with the responsibility of promoting a welcoming open-door policy to anybody wanting to take that next tentative step towards acceptance into the worldwide family of Christ."

And with that, she left.

There was a thoughtful silence.

"I think Margaret's got a point," said Lesley at length. "It is wrong for us to question the motives of the couple, and of course we mustn't lose sight of the real reason why we sing at these weddings." I was rather touched, I must admit. Until she turned to Rachel, and with a mischievous grin went on "With the dosh from the next three, I can afford that dress out of my catalogue!"

I kept a diplomatic silence. So, thankfully, did Tripplehorn. In the circumstances I guessed my proposal regarding the fees would have gone down just about as well as an offer by the bar staff of the Titanic to pop up on deck to replenish the empty ice buckets.

Monday 31ˢᵗ March

Margaret rang me first thing to ask how I'd got on in trying to persuade the choir to donate some of their wedding fees to the vestry fund. She'd obviously overheard my conversation with Tripplehorn yesterday. I told her that I really was facing an uphill battle with the fundraising just now, and things hadn't been helped by a phone call I'd had last night from the vicar saying that the lottery grant they'd been counting on is likely to be considerably less than was hoped.

"To be honest," I said, "I just don't know if I can do this."

"Of course you can," she answered. "One simple word. Prayer."

"I've thought of that," I said. "But I never quite know how or what to pray. There are so many deserving causes. If God answers my prayer and people give to me, what about the prayers of all the other fundraisers who were after the money I've been given? Does that mean that their prayers haven't been answered?"

"Of course not," said Margaret earnestly. "God is working and will continue to work in you and for you. In fact, I wouldn't be surprised if things started happening sooner than you think. I tell you what. Come round to my house on Thursday. It's our fifth Lent group meeting. We're talking about prayer and this week it's about how God answers prayer. We'd really love to see you, and I think you'd learn a lot."

Well, I did ask for it.

Amongst the junk mail that came into the office this morning was a flyer from Fry Away in Trenchard Street, now the only chippie in town following the closure of Come Fry With Me four months ago. To celebrate its recent refurbishment, the shop is offering sizeable discounts on bulk orders of takeaway meals, and free delivery. Was about to throw it in the bin when I suddenly realised its potential, not for a lunchtime office beano but for a fundraising evening consisting of a fish-and-chip supper combined perhaps with a light-hearted musical quiz for the choir and their families and friends.

I rang Ruth in the evening to get a second opinion on it.

"Sounds all right to me," she said. "Only you need to be careful with your questions. Don't do what my friend April did and ask a question with more than one right answer."

"If it happens, it happens," I laughed. "We just scrap the question and ask another."

"Not if it's the sudden-death question following a tie in a quiz final, as hers was," she said. "It took at least three deep cleans to scrape the remains of battered cod from off the hall ceiling. And to wash the ketchup stains off the walls."

"Feelings must have been running very high," I observed.

"Oh yes," she replied. "They take no prisoners at the Catholic Mothers' Wednesday Fellowship."

Thursday 3rd April

Margaret's Lent group meeting tonight. I wasn't hugely looking forward to it, but with my fundraising campaign as bogged down as it was, I certainly felt in need of some divine help and any avenue was better than none. For some reason I had expected a large gathering but in fact, besides myself, only the leader and three others, including Margaret, were present. It was the first time I'd been to Margaret's house, and although I had expected it to reflect her very profound Christian commitment, I was still quite taken aback by the profusion of Christian texts on the walls, and the number of works of Christian literature that were packed into the bookshelves. On a board in the corner of the front room was a piece of paper headed PRAYER INTENTIONS and I noticed that every single member of the choir was mentioned, though whether there was any significance in the order in which the names were written I couldn't say. Languishing in the relegation zone near the foot of the page were the Ellises and Eileen Crosby, but even though I knew them all to be well-balanced and contented folk, largely untouched by life's tragedies, I don't think that one should necessarily infer they were any less in need of prayer than other choir members. By the same token I would feel uncomfortable if I thought Margaret felt I had a special call on her time of daily conversation with the Lord, notwithstanding my appearance amongst those vying for one of the automatic promotion places.

The leader, whom I vaguely recognised as having preached at St Basil's the year before last, explained that the theme of tonight's meeting was "Don't Be Afraid To Ask." He explained that we cannot expect God to answer our prayers unless we are totally frank with Him about our needs and wishes, and prayer that skates over what we really feel and simply deals with the things we think God wants to hear is not real prayer at all. By way of illustration, he asked us to write down on a piece of paper one thing we really desired in our heart, however silly or trivial it might sound, and the whole group would commit it to God in prayer.

A few moments later the papers were handed in and the leader read them out.

"Our first prayer," he said, "is for justice for the world's poor; for a new commitment to reducing or remitting Third World debt; to an end to policies and practices that widen the gulf between the haves and have-nots; and for a greater spirit of Christian giving amongst the wealthy. Our second prayer is for victims of war and violence; for those left bereaved, orphaned or displaced by man's barbarism and selfishness; for a renewed dialogue between warring nations, that disputes between men and women of different religions and political affiliations may be resolved without recourse to bloodshed. Our third prayer is for the victims of natural disaster; for a greater understanding of the causes of them and for more money to be set aside to predict and respond appropriately to them; for continued research into those factors which bring about harmful climate change and upset the climactical equilibrium upon which the continuation of life of our planet is so dependent.

"And our fourth prayer is for a generous discount from Fry Away for the fish-and-chip supper."

Friday 4th April

With the sound of prayers for God's blessing on the fish-and-chip supper and quiz still ringing in my ears from last night, I rang the vicarage to book the church hall for the event for the first Saturday in May, only to be told that Cora's empire has now spread to the church hall as well and that I needed to speak to her to make the necessary arrangements. With some trepidation I approached her at tonight's choir practice.

"Well, of course, the church hall is very busy at this time of year," she said, withdrawing a large black diary from her Waitrose carrier bag and flicking through the pages. "I very much doubt there's anything at all I can offer you this side of the beginning of June. There's weddings most Saturdays. The Scouts have a disco on the first Friday in May, the bridge club are in there every Thursday afternoon, there's country dancing classes each Wednesday night, Mrs Blitheman's sewing class on Tuesday mornings, Miss Livermore's mother and baby classes on Monday afternoons, Mr Codrington's Life Enhancer Business Breakfast Seminars on alternate Thursdays......booked solid. No. Wait a minute. I tell a lie. I think there is a cancellation on the evening of Tuesday April 29th. You can have the hall from 6.45 but not a moment earlier."

Unable to resist humouring her, I replied "Presumably to allow a good hour from the estimated departure time of the last guests for the reception following the thanksgiving services for the successful removal of Madge Oglethorpe's ingrowing toenail."

"I've got that booked in for the 28th," she snapped.

At choir tonight I told everyone what was being organised. I explained I wanted to keep the quiz itself very informal, participants will work in teams, we'll have a nice long break for fish and chips, and hopefully there'll be time for a few jars at the Holly Tree afterwards, making it a really nice sociable evening. We agreed that it would be appropriate, as the quiz night is for the benefit of choir members and their friends, for it to be a musical quiz, although we decided we wouldn't restrict ourselves to church music and could include questions on music generally, both classical and popular. I said I would be happy to be quiz master and set the questions, ensuring that each team got a good balance of church music and non-church music in its quota. "Having said that," I said, "I'm quite happy for you to suggest questions to me between now and the night, to save me a bit of time."

In retrospect, this statement proved to be tactically a little unwise, for no sooner had we finished the rehearsal than I was approached firstly by Cora with a set of hopelessly difficult questions on the later operas of Richard Wagner, then by Matthew Sparkes asking if we can include the question "Who wrote Haydn's Trumpet Concerto" in the hope that it'll fool at least one unsuspecting team of musical experts, and finally by Henry Peasgood who said I should ask how many hymns can be sung to the tune Gonfalon Royal. "I think the definitive total is 29," he said, "and what's more, as of last Wednesday when I sang it at a funeral in London, I can confidently say I've sung every one of them."

I can just see the editors of *Who's Who* now. Desperately trying to hold the print of the new edition to accommodate all the details.

Sunday 6th April

Woke feeling somewhat guilty this morning. Following my wasted day off a fortnight ago, I'd spent much of yesterday working on *Spirit Of Fire*, and hadn't even spoken to Katie. So I felt it was the least I could do to ring her first thing and invite her to join me for tea at Maggie's Pantry, a tea shop in a remote village fourteen miles away. The shop had just had a rave write-up in the local paper, with Maggie's fluffy cheese scones and creamy home-made butter being described as "delectable."

Having been interrupted in the middle of my work yesterday by the postman bringing Melvyn Samlesbury's music, I brought it with me to church this morning for Tripplehorn to look at. He gave it a cursory glance and said "I think we can live with this. Okay then, could you do enough copies for the whole choir then let me have them later on today so I can start working on them before our next practice." And moments later I found it thrust back at me. All 12 compositions.

At least, it being a Sunday, there was no queue for the office copier and Katie had found an absorbing article to read in her Sunday paper on the subject of assertiveness, while I was doing the copying. Even so, I wasn't in the best of moods at the start of the exercise. And when after the sixth copy of the eighteenth page of the second piece the machine took upon itself to run out of toner, and then proceeded to jam after the twelfth copy of the tenth page of the third piece, I ran out of patience completely. "This is ridiculous," I fumed. "It's supposed to be my day off, for goodness sake."

By way of response, Katie thrust the assertiveness article in front of me. "Look, here you are," she said. "This piece has got loads of tips on how to assert yourself. Why don't you try it? Ring Frank and tell him you're not doing it. He can jolly well do the copies himself, at his own expense, if he needs them so badly."

I perused the article, then got on to the phone to our choirmaster and told him I just wasn't able or willing to give up any more of my Sunday afternoon. "I'm not trying to be awkward," I said, reading almost verbatim from the page in front of me. "I quite understand why you want this music now, but I have to think of my own needs and management of my own time. I think it's unreasonable to expect the burden of this task to fall predominantly on to my shoulders, and perhaps I can leave you on this occasion to think about how the work could be divided more fairly so I can spend my leisure time as I want to spend it."

Since it took me another two hours to finish the job and deliver to him the complete photocopied sets, each one hole-punched and in plastic folders, and another ten minutes to fill out the application form for the assertiveness course as advertised in Katie's paper, it was clear that we were going to struggle to reach Maggie's Pantry before it shut. We just made it, thanks to a spirited 50mph dash along Cattle Creep Lane, but by the time we got there they were only serving tea and cakes with no sign of Maggie's delectable fluffy cheese scones and creamy home-made butter, the last of which had apparently gone a good twenty minutes before. Mortified, I suggested to Katie that we go back to town and have a nice evening meal in the Crown, but it was too late. Angrily she replied "Oh, let's just forget it for today. Go home and get on with your stupid vestry fundraising and when you've got it out of your system, perhaps then you might think about putting me first for a change."

Got home feeling thoroughly miserable, my humour not improved at all by the arrival of Craig Dumbleton an hour or so later. A copy of the questions used in the music rounds of the annual quiz nights of the South East London Railway Arts Association between 1970 and 1981 seemed a poor substitute for Maggie's culinary delights or the Crown's equally taste bud tickling toffee pavlova, especially when half of the questions seemed singularly parochial in nature. Never mind. If Cora's team and Craig's team are tied in the lead at the end of the contest, I might just use as a tie-breaker Question 12 in the 1973 batch and ask whether it was Ophelia Rumbold or Dolores Bracegirdle who played the female lead in the Honor Oak Park Thespians' 1966 premiere of the musical *Dr Thundergherkin And The Poisoned Trouser Press.* If for no other reason, just to see the look on Cora's face.

Friday 11th April

I had hoped to finish *Spirit Of Fire* tomorrow, but after Sunday's debacle I decided I must set tomorrow aside to take Katie out and have a day off today to get the writing done. I certainly won't be in the mood to tackle it during Holy Week with its hectic schedule of choir commitments, beginning with two big services on Palm Sunday in two days' time.

Got off to a prompt start at 7.30am, and kept going almost non-stop for the next ten hours, with only one brief break for a takeaway sandwich from the bakery and some batteries for my little keyboard which I was using throughout the day. I had to draw quite deeply on my memories of the 'O' level harmony tuition that had been provided to me by the somewhat disorganised Mr Masters, whose star turn had been to book the school choir to sing the services at Hereford Cathedral for a weekend, only to arrive after months of rehearsal to find we'd been double-booked with the Konigskappellchor of Saarbrucken. But I also felt I was drawing inspiration from Margaret's prayers, Katie's loving encouragement – well, up to the cheese scone fiasco, anyway – and my own renewed commitment to God during this solemn time of Lent. I would love to say that as the notes flowed from my black Pentel on to the music manuscript paper, as supplied by George Proudfoot & Sons Stationers in Muggleton Lane, I had some great Handelian vision of the Lord in all His glorious majesty, but sadly I didn't. And I can't somehow see my descendants being the least bit interested in the fact that the only interruption to my work had consisted of a cold-caller congratulating me on winning the chance to commit myself to an eight-hour timeshare presentation in the Prescott Room of the Holiday Inn, Bracknell.

Carried away by the euphoria of having completed the work, I decided to take it with me to choir tonight, and asked Tripplehorn if he'd play it over on the organ while I was getting the coffee ready. It didn't sound too bad at all, and I even got a little round of applause from Rachel who was standing nearby. Tripplehorn got down off the organ stool, said "You've done your best. You can't ask for any more than that," and disappeared into the vestry.

I was absolutely gutted by his dismissive comment. Rachel saw how distraught I looked, and as I was washing up said to me "Don't worry. He'd have said it about Bach's first Brandenburg Concerto if that had been presented to him."

"M'yes," Matthew Sparkes chimed in, "but he probably wouldn't have said behind Bach's back that he had about as much future in the world of composition as a clockwork octopus."

Palm Sunday 13th April

After a lovely time with Katie yesterday, a big sing today: the traditional Palm Sunday procession followed by a lengthy service including a plainchant recital of the Passion story in St Matthew's Gospel, a rehearsal all afternoon, and then tonight a performance of Charles Wood's setting of the Passion according to St Mark. I must say I find it a markedly superior work to Stainer's *Crucifixion*, which we usually perform on Palm Sunday, and I was pleased that Tripplehorn had decided we should have a change from the Stainer this year.

During one of the many stops in the afternoon rehearsal, Matthew asked "Did they really have sandwiches and sausages on sticks in Jesus' time?"

When I asked him what he meant, he pointed to the section we'd been singing, concerning the reaction of the crowd to Jesus, and said "Look, it says here. 'And some began to buffet him.'"

Although I feel ashamed to have to say it, I was quite preoccupied for most of the rest of the practice with a wholly absurd and plainly irreverent mental picture of a table of assorted savouries laid out in the blazing Jerusalem sunshine and the angry crowd expressing their displeasure by hurling assorted canapés into the air.

An unexpected and welcome boost for the vestry fund tonight. After the performance, which was well attended, a retiring collection was taken, and it was announced that it would be divided between our link parish in West Africa and the vestry fund. The vicar said that a new vestry was "vital to help and support the choir for future generations." I hope it was that, rather than our performance tonight, which prompted one middle-aged man to shove a fiver on to the plate and comment "You clearly need all the help you can get."

As there was just one more week of Lenten sacrifices to go, I reminded the choir that sponsor money was due as soon as possible after Easter Sunday, hoping that this might in fact prompt one or two choir members to start getting some sponsors. There again, judging by Irving Cattermole's moaning about the shambolic Palm procession through the town centre this morning, which had had to be diverted along the deserted Back Lane as a result of essential weekend roadworks, I shouldn't think he's going to need to be troubling too many people for sponsorship money for curbing his sarcastic comments during Lent. And I doubt Cora Willoughby-Smith will be needing specialist investment advice regarding any funds she's likely to have collected for singing above top D sharp without going at least a semitone out of tune.

At least Arthur Ramsbottom had something to offer tonight, namely the penultimate chapter of his choir history which he told me dealt with the 1980's. As he gave me the chapter he remarked "A good little Lenten task, this." It was left to me to work out whether he was referring to his task of writing it or my task of attempting to decipher what he had written. Looking at the quality of his work so far, I can see the potential for the project to be a financial disaster. If the church itself is happy to pay for the printing, as Tripplehorn has indicated is likely, that's fine. But with so much unrest among parishioners about the way their financial contributions are being spent, it's a big risk for the PCC, and if it flopped

I suspect they themselves would take quite a buffeting. And that an angry volley of vol-au-vents and chucking of chicken nuggets at the Annual Church Meeting would be the least of their worries.

Maundy Thursday 17th April

Met Katie for lunch today. She told me she'd seen an article in the local paper about an Emmaus walk that is planned for Easter Monday, its name being derived from the famous story in Luke chapter 24 in which two disciples were joined by the resurrected Christ on the Emmaus road but failed to recognise him. The walk is intended to be essentially a meditative one, with occasional stops for prayer and reflection on the life of the risen Christ before His ascension. She suggested that we organise a choir Easter Monday walk along the route planned for the choir walk next month, and throw in two or three pub visits on the way. We could check out the pubs for possible visiting on the choir walk and might even do a bit of informal singing in the pubs in aid of the vestry fund. Although, as I understand it, nowhere in Luke 24 is there any mention of pub stops on the Emmaus journey, I liked the idea and told Katie I'd mention it at choir tonight. As soon as I got home I checked out the route for the choir walk and saw no less than three pubs on or close to it. Provided we keep a good pace on Monday, it does seem we should be able to visit all three comfortably during opening hours.

Before our Maundy Thursday service this evening we reached a compromise over the wedding fees. There is to be a very big wedding in church on the 22nd November and we've agreed that our fees for this wedding, and this one only, will be donated straight to the vestry fund. Pleased that the matter had been resolved, I felt in just the right frame of mind for the service and I found it immensely moving. It was a shame that it had to be followed somewhat anticlimactically by a rehearsal for all the music for Good Friday and Easter Sunday. Mercifully, the Holy Saturday liturgy was to be said this year. By 9.50pm we'd just staggered through to the end of the Good Friday music, and with Tripplehorn telling us we wouldn't be going home till we'd got through Easter Sunday's music, I saw my chances of selling the Emmaus walk as somewhat lower than those of a salesman in the depths of the Sahara successfully flogging a consignment of fire-damaged end-of-line plastic mackintoshes. Rallying somewhat, we rounded off Psalm 150, at the end of the Easter Sunday worship, at twenty past ten, but by then I only had the strength to give Monday's walk a half-hearted mention and not one single person expressed any interest.

Much to my surprise, Tripplehorn told me afterwards that my *Spirit Of Fire* was growing on him. "It's not bad at all," he said. "Obviously that's after about six times playing it over, and the punters will only hear it the once. But still, I think it might work. I've a few suggestions to make and I'll run through them with you after the service tomorrow."

I asked him if there was anything specific he wanted to suggest.

"Get rid of that awful slushy scrunchy rubbish at the top of page four," he said. "If you were one my GCSE examinees I'd fail you on that straight away."

I boldly suggested that by the same token he'd probably have failed Benjamin Britten as well.

"I wouldn't have entered him for the exam to begin with," he replied.

Staggered home, ate an enormous cheese sandwich, and went straight to bed, dreaming of Craig Dumbleton dressed up as Pontius Pilate and dispensing teas in a British Rail buffet car.

Good Friday 18th April

Although one could never call the Good Friday liturgy enjoyable, and my spirits were not lifted by the continued lack of interest in Monday's walk, I still found today's act of worship enriching and rewarding. I was so pleased that Katie came along and even more pleased that, with the promise of her home-made hot cross buns at her house afterwards, I had the perfect excuse to duck out of Cora Willoughby-Smith's traditional Good Friday tea-and-making-travesty-of-grand-opera party.

Before going back to Katie's, I got together with Tripplehorn to discuss my composition.

"To short-circuit things a bit, I've done some rewriting of certain sections," he said. "See what you think." He then proceeded to play the amended version on the organ. To my delight and relief, most of it sounded just as it had done when he'd first played it over a week ago, and the amendments he'd made improved the overall quality considerably. I told him he should be billed as co-writer of the piece and take a share of the prize money if the piece won the competition, but he wouldn't hear of it. "No, it's your piece, and you must take the credit," he said. He went on to say that he would personally deliver the piece to Anthony Cartwright that evening, and also said he'd have no hesitation in recommending that my piece be awarded the prize. He can be such a pain when he wants to be, but I was immensely touched by his generosity on this occasion.

In a burst of confidence, I told him I was surprised he'd allowed so many of the unison sections to stay in. "To tell you the truth," I said, "when I've come across long unison passages in other composers' works, I just assumed it was the composer being a bit lazy."

"Heavens, no," Tripplehorn said. "Unison sections are very important. They symbolise a sense of unity between the singers, proclaiming that they are as one in their offer of thanks and praise to God." He paused, then added "And they give rubbish choirs the chance to regroup when the singers have got five bars behind the organ by the end of page two."

Easter Sunday 20th April

A wonderful service this morning. Refreshed by a good night's sleep, and delighted with Katie's mouth-watering Easter chocolates, I could not have felt more positive about our worship. Just when I thought things couldn't get any better, Anthony Cartwright informed me I'd won the anthem prize with my *Spirit Of Fire* and produced a cheque which was double what I'd expected.

Brian and Rachel invited Katie and me for lunch, along with Ken and his wife. It was a dull, grey afternoon and a feeling of lethargy and slight anticlimax set in, with none of us feeling up to a walk after a delicious meal. But we were in fact able to utilise the next couple of hours very profitably indeed, agreeing many more quiz questions for the 29th, and by quarter past four or so, when we decided to stop for a drink, I had probably more questions than I needed. "I've a good one," said Rachel as she went to put the kettle on. "Name the person you remember with a sinking heart you'd invited round for tea and Easter cake at half past four just as you wanted to veg out with a glass of Alka Seltzer and the *Sunday Times* and who appears at the window with a carrier bag full of his prized choir outing videos."

And seconds later Arthur Ramsbottom was among those present.

By ten past seven, even Katie, who had had mercifully little experience of the St Basil's choir archive material, was wilting at the sight of Iris Higginbotham's sandalled feet trudging along Broadstairs High Street.

Easter Monday 21st April

With Brian and Rachel telling me they were going off to East Anglia for four days, Arthur Ramsbottom advising that he was travelling to see his sister on the Isle of Wight, and Hazel Ledworthy barking down the phone that Monday was her toenail-cutting day, the support for the walk was diminishing by the minute. Indeed when Katie and I arrived at the start there was nobody else there at all.

"To be honest, I'm quite relieved," said Katie. "Let's just have a quick walk and then go back to Crispin's in town for coffee and their gorgeous hot bacon sandwiches."

Content with this suggestion, I was just locking my car when, to my horror, another vehicle drew up behind us and out stepped Henry Peasgood accompanied by a middle-aged man dressed in a very greasy Barbour jacket, skin-tight trousers and faded white trainers. Having apologised for his lateness, Henry introduced his companion to us as Giles, a staunch real ale enthusiast who'd been staying with him over the

Easter weekend. "You gave the impression on Good Friday that you were rather desperate for some company today," Henry told me. Apparently Giles, having heard about the proposed pub stops, was keen to add to his collection of hostelries he'd visited in Great Britain as part of his fieldwork for his forthcoming publication, *One Thousand Pubs To Visit Before You Die.*

Four and a half hours later, I suspect he'd decided that prospective purchasers of his book could quite happily go to their graves without having sampled the delights of the Apple Tree, the Cow And Daisy (supposedly a corruption of Count Tessy, an Austrian noble who was believed to have bedded a local farm girl in a nearby barn in 1878, if the plaque above the bar was to be believed) and the Blacksmith's Arms. The Apple Tree, which we reached five minutes after it opened, was a real spit-and-sawdust affair. It boasted just one other customer, a man in his fifties who was sitting at the bar, looking somewhat lugubriously into his pint. To try and cheer him up, I introduced ourselves and told him what we were doing today.

"To be honest," the man replied, "and I hope you won't be offended, but I am totally disillusioned with the way in which the Church has set its agenda in terms of spending its available funds. And no wonder the congregations are deserting it in droves because of its total inability to put the wider interests of the community before its own self-serving and self-indulgent ends." With that, he downed the rest of his beer and stalked grumpily away towards the toilets.

I turned to the barman and, pointing in the direction taken by our erstwhile drinking companion, enquired "Just who on earth does he think he is?"

"Oh, him," said the barman. "He's the local archdeacon."

We departed suitably hastily, and headed for the Cow And Daisy. Giles was proving to be every bit as tedious as feared, totally obsessed as he was with his wretched pub project, though thankfully he at least confined the majority of his observations to Henry and left Katie and me to keep each other company. We got to the Cow And Daisy at ten past one, in perfect time for lunch, but had been beaten to it by a very substantial deputation from the local clay pigeon shoot enjoying its Easter Monday meet. It took me twenty minutes to fight my way through a crowd of people six deep at the bar to get in our drinks order, and there followed a wait of similar duration at a separate hatch to place our requests for food. It was fortunate that I hadn't parted with my money before hearing an announcement that order number 76 was ready for collection and then noticing that the order chit I was about to be given bore the number 115. Having decided to cancel the food order, I was still faced with the task of getting our drinks back to our outside table. By the time I'd negotiated a temporary contraflow system necessitated by recovery work on a plate of sausage ploughmans currently abandoned on the southbound carriageway, and been forced into a diversion via the snug bar owing to the shedding by a fellow traveller of a quantity of mixed vegetables across all four lanes and the hard shoulder, my patience and my spirits, as well as my enthusiasm for entertaining the pub customers in song, were at rock bottom. And not improved at all, when we finally left, by Giles' recital of the 239 things that were wrong with the beer we had just consumed.

And so to the Blacksmith's, reached at just before three, barely two minutes before it shut for the rest of the afternoon. Two minutes, though, in which Henry and Giles managed to order their fourth and fifth pints of the day respectively and, like all the others before them, at my expense. Presumably Henry felt it was the least I could do in return for the pleasure of their company. But although we now had some useful information on the quality of the pubs which will help in planning our walk next month, namely to steer well clear of all three, the vestry fund hadn't been helped at all, and as Katie pointed out, we'd have done better financially simply by staying at home.

Still, Katie and I got our hot bacon sandwich. Even if it was six hours later than planned, and not at Crispin's but at the Cassons Park Trading Estate Burger King. Of which there was most emphatically no mention in Luke chapter 24.

Friday 25th April

At choir tonight I asked if any outstanding money for Lenten sacrifices could be with me by Sunday at the latest.

"Oh yes, sorry, I was going to tell you," said Alison. "My giving up chocolate went by the board when I was invited to go with Matthew's class to a tour of the Bournville factory about two weeks before Easter."

Eileen Crosby cleared her throat. "Er – it's confession time from me as well," she said. "I did say I'd pack in my evening tipple of whisky for Lent. I had lots of sponsors for it. But then I met Dorothy Dunmore who I'd not seen since college and she took me out for a drink in the Badgers Rest. The day after Mothering Sunday."

"Did anyone else manage to get any sponsorship at all?" I enquired, looking meaningfully at Brian and Rachel who looked splendidly tanned from their mini-break at Great Yarmouth.

"Oh – er – yes," said Brian, producing a collection of coins from his pocket and thrusting them in my direction.

Afterwards in the pub I felt it was the least I could do to buy him a drink as a token of thanks for his loyalty and support. After we'd downed a well-earned pint, I went to the bar to buy another round, but chanced to overhear Brian say to Craig "I would have bought the next round, but I gave all my money away at choir. I hadn't the heart to confess I'd not raised any sponsor money."

I couldn't resist telling Rachel, out of Brian's hearing, that I'd happened to hear this conversation and I was quite touched that he should have come to my rescue and saved my face at the practice by his cash contribution despite the failure of his sponsorship efforts.

"Oh, he gave it his best shot," said Rachel. "He was actually sponsoring himself not to slag Frank Tripplehorn off during Lent. It was tough, too, I can tell you. He was doing pretty well and although there were occasions when I thought he'd crack, he really stuck at it. Quite often I had to restrain him at critical moments and that in itself was no mean feat. It was only when Frank rang him up over some ridiculous matter when he was still in bed that, under intolerable pressure, he finally gave in."

"And when was that?" I asked her.

"About twenty past seven on Ash Wednesday morning," she replied.

Sunday 27th April

A pretty flat service this morning, predictably perhaps. However, no shortage of customers for Tuesday's quiz and fish-and-chip supper, and it was with good heart that this evening I rang Fry Away with my order.

"Right, are you ready for this?" I announced proudly, to the woman who answered the phone. "Seven sausage and chips, five with salt, one with salt and vinegar, one with neither. Twenty fish and chips, twelve with salt, six with salt and vinegar, two with neither. Fourteen chicken and chips, nine with salt, four with salt and vinegar, one with vinegar. Two steak and kidney pies and chips, both with salt and vinegar. Four portions of chips on their own, two with salt, two with salt and vinegar. Eleven portions of mushy peas. Four portions of baked beans. Sixteen cans of Lilt, of which ten should be Diet Lilt. Ten cans of Fanta and two cans of dandelion and burdock. And if you could deliver it to St Basil's church hall for eight fifteen that would be brilliant."

"And you want this when?" she asked me.

"Tuesday," I said.

"Ah. Slight problem," she said. "We're shut on Tuesdays."

That certainly is a problem. As is the team allocation. I suppose it was my fault for inviting participants to state their team preference, although since certain combinations of individuals would have started a civil war within two minutes of sitting down, I felt fully justified in taking at least some preventative steps. What perhaps I'd not been prepared for was the vehemence with which certain competitors expressed their desire not to be paired with named others, or insisted on conditions attaching to their willingness to work with them. Some of the conditions had been drafted with such apparent precision that I half wondered if the services of a senior QC had been obtained for the purpose of preparing them. I would have thought the smell of chip fat will completely nullify the effect of Cora Willoughby-Smith's sister's perfume which Henry Peasgood is apparently so anxious not to have to inhale during the course of the proceedings. But I confess I secretly have some sympathy with Irving Cattermole's wish not to be teamed with Joan Trumpington unless she enters into a solemn and binding undertaking not to slurp on or snuffle, sniff, snivel or drool over any hot or chilled beverage or any wholly or partially liquid foodstuff that may be dispensed to her at all such times as she is in his line of vision, or within 25 metres of him, or both, as the case may be.

Tuesday 29th April
Having tried first thing yesterday to persuade Fry Away to provide the food on its closing day, I'd been advised that they'd consider it but would only ring me back in the unlikely event of their being able to oblige. Since I'd heard nothing from them by midday today, I got hold of The Other Plaice, a takeaway in the next town, just before lunch, and they not only said they were open tonight but would deliver the order at 8.15pm.

Mightily relieved, I spent most of my afternoon off checking and double-checking all the evening's arrangements, including verifying the answer to every quiz question and ensuring no question was to be assigned to a participant who'd supplied it in the first place. At 5pm, just when I thought I'd covered every eventuality, I got a call from Miranda Cobbledick, an ex-choir member, self-appointed leader of the close harmony singers which called themselves the Load Of Old Cobblers, and sworn enemy of Cora Willoughby-Smith, asking if there was any reason why she could not form a team and come along. Apparently Arthur Ramsbottom, who at Rachel's on Easter Sunday had asked if ex-choir members were eligible, had tipped her off, and fearful of turning away much needed vestry fund money, I told her that as a former chorister she could. I even went as far as to phone The Other Plaice for additional supplies.

The plan was to have four rounds of questions before supper and another three afterwards. After two rounds Craig Dumbleton's team, the Puffing Billies, were well out in front, but their lead was cut back spectacularly after round three by Lesley Markwick's team the Weakest Links, and by the time I saw the van belonging to The Other Plaice arrive at ten past eight, any one of the teams was in with an excellent chance.

As I announced the break, Joan Trumpington approached me and asked why we were stopping. When I told her that we were stopping for food, she said "I arranged with Chipadeedoodah that they would be here for

eight thirty, that was all. As choir secretary, I assumed you were happy to leave the catering arrangements with me."

And when Fry Away appeared two minutes later with a van bearing the complete order I asked for, together with a bill containing a 20% surcharge for coming out on their closing night, I found myself rapidly rewriting the miracle of the feeding of the five thousand and, worse, staring at a potentially devastating blow to the financial success of the evening.

As I surveyed the formidable array of newspaper-wrapped foodstuffs, which multiplied as Chipadeedoodah's delivery arrived, Tripplehorn sidled up to me. "I was in Fry Away yesterday lunchtime," he said. "I often go there and they know me very well. They did tell me they could manage our order and when I saw Joan last night I mentioned it to her. I assumed she'd let you know."

All we could do was to ask people to eat what they could. Matthew Sparkes nobly ate three portions of chicken and chips without flinching, but even he was beginning to wilt after downing his second saveloy sausage. Rachel Ellis said she'd never frozen takeaway steak and kidney pies, or indeed pots of mushy peas, but she diplomatically said she'd give it a try. The assistant priest, having preached on Sunday about the horrors of waste and overindulgence in contemporary Western society, was forced to choose between eating either his words or a Chipadeedoodah chicken leg soaked in congealed grease. I threw in the towel after forcing down two pieces of vinegar-soaked haddock, an amply proportioned hot dog, and a bulging carton of Fry Away chips that had the appetising texture of wooden clothes pegs.

We got under way again, the leftovers consisting not of twelve basketfuls but sixteen bin-liner-hastily-bought-from-Handysave-fuls, and at length came to the last round which included the question "Which is the first of the Savoy operas by Gilbert and Sullivan?"

Then the fun started. As I read out the answer I had in front of me, *Trial By Jury,* there were loud cheers from Miranda Cobbledick and her entourage, but howls of protest from Cora Willoughby-Smith's table.

"*Trial By Jury* was not the first Savoy opera," Cora bellowed. "It was *Patience.* That was the first opera performed at the new Savoy Theatre so the ones before can't properly be called Savoy operas."

"Ah," said Miranda, "but all the Gilbert and Sullivan operas are generically referred to as the Savoy operas. So technically *Trial By Jury* is correct, being the first Gilbert and Sullivan opera."

"Except," said Henry Peasgood, who I knew had to put his twopenn'orth in, "that *Trial By Jury* wasn't their first collaboration. It was *Thespis.* So Miranda's team have got it wrong anyway!"

"He never asked that," Miranda protested. "He asked which IS the first of the operas. The music for *Thespis* got lost so technically it doesn't exist any more."

"The words still survive," said Henry, "and they're certainly in my *Collected Works Of Gilbert And Sullivan* I've got at home."

"They're not in mine," Miranda retorted.

"Can I suggest a compromise?" I put in. "Let's scrap the question and I'll ask another. I think that's...."

"No, I'm sorry, I can't accept that," interrupted Miranda. "The answer you've got is *Trial By Jury*. That's what we've written down, so we're entitled to the point."

"That's nonsensical," said Cora. "If it's wrong it's wrong. You can't get a point for an answer that's patently wrong."

"That's always been your trouble," said Miranda. "You always think you're right and everyone else is wrong. Well, let me remind you..."

Within five minutes, despite the best efforts of the vicar and myself to restore order, and the fact that the allocation of a point to Miranda's team would have not the slightest bearing on the result, the quiz had disintegrated into uproar; not only were previous quiz evening skulduggeries brought into the equation, but also other ignominious past squabbles between the two including the tampering with the elderberry wine at the 1991 church produce sale, the rigged judging of the 1987 Easter bonnet parade, and the incident during the 1997 St Flavian Infants' School reunion involving the mouldy pork pie and the melting Jaffa Cakes.

Nor did I, as the final adjudicator, escape scot-free. By the end of the evening, I found myself threatened with the full gamut of sanctions for my unforgivable error: a steadfast refusal by Miranda or her team to have anything to do with future fundraising initiatives in which I had any dealings, a damning report in the church magazine exposing my stupidity and negligence, a civil action for damages in the High Court for defamation of character, and an appeal to the European Court Of Justice in Strasbourg against my gross violations of human rights to fair and equal treatment.

But at least there were no traces of battered cod on the ceiling.

MAY

Friday 2nd May

The start of a Bank Holiday weekend. Tripplehorn hurried through Sunday's music and I am sure I was not alone in hoping that he was proposing to let us out early. But instead he insisted we spend time preparing for Mervyn Samlesbury's workshop next Saturday, and distributed copies of one of his works, *Lord Let Me Know Mine End*.

"Why have we got to do this now, Mum?" Matthew Sparkes grumbled. Alison simply shrugged, whereupon Matthew took the music he had just been given and imitated the sound of paper being torn. It was a trick I had seen performed countless times and had almost always managed to fall for, although I liked to feel I might be a little wiser to it by now. On this occasion, however, Matthew's impression was astonishingly convincing – partially, one suspects, because a slip of his fingers caused his copy of *Lord Let Me Know Mine End* to be ripped unceremoniously in two.

As a result of information received from an unnamed source, Tripplehorn proceeded at once to the scene of the crime. For one hideous moment I thought I saw him raising his hand in readiness to administer a type of punishment unheard of at St Basil's since Phineas Meade-Ratchett had caught Roddy McIntosh nibbling a Walnut Whip in the middle of Alex Abercrombie's arpeggios. Fortunately, however, following an earnest plea in mitigation by the accused, the sentence was commuted to a formal reprimand and a financial penalty representing the notional cost of photocopying a further set of music, to be paid by direct weekly deduction from pocket money commencing within seven calendar days.

By ten past nine, I realised that Matthew had by his actions anticipated what in fact was rapidly to become the collective view of all of us as to Melvyn's Samlesbury's competence as a contemporary composer. Even Lesley Markwick was forced to agree with Alison's comment that the work was as turgid as a pair of Y fronts left out on a Grimsby washing line during a snowstorm. And no more aesthetically pleasing.

Sunday 4th May

Following a rather pedestrian service this morning – the absence of one or two sopranos meant we had to fall back on *Lead Me Lord* for the third Sunday this year – Tripplehorn called us together to firm up the catering arrangements for next Saturday. We all earnestly wanted to avoid a repetition of last Tuesday's shambles. Ruth Hartnell volunteered to do some cooking for us and reeled off a list of the recipes she had in mind to render the day, if nothing else, a gastronomic triumph; Craig Dumbleton offered to enlist the services of his intimate gourmet acquaintances Mr Kipling, Mr Cadbury and Mr Happy Shopper; and Irving Cattermole said if it was all the same to everyone else he would prefer to go home and have a ham sandwich in front of the 1.30 at Kempton Park. From the murmurs of agreement which followed, it seemed he was far from being alone.

"Personally, I think that's a shame," said Tripplehorn. "I see the communal lunch as being an integral part of the day in helping to cement relationships among choir members and demonstrate our commitment to solidarity in moving forward the musical aspects of the church's outreach to the community."

I hope he's still saying that if he finds himself in the target area of anyone who's just digested a portion of Ruth Hartnell's Gruyere Cheese and Kidney Bean Surprise.

Tonight I got a phone call from Melvyn Samlesbury. Not only did he reiterate how much he is looking forward to his visit, but he also said he was proposing to attend our rehearsal on the night before and was prepared to offer us, for a small fee in addition to the payment we were already pledging to provide him, a "critical appraisal of the choir's rehearsal techniques and discipline."

I decided that from a financial standpoint it would not be politic to agree, even though it had been decided to boost the profits for the day by inviting members of this morning's congregation to come and observe the workshop, and then contribute to a retiring collection. Moreover, I was somewhat apprehensive at how well an appraisal would go down with the less thick-skinned choir members. The prospect of actually having to make further inroads into the vestry fund profit margin, and risk losing loyal members of the choir, for the privilege of being formally advised *inter alia* that Matthew Sparkes should be made to refrain from keeping an audible count of the number of times we are ordered to sing over Sunday's psalm chant would be quite unthinkable. Though part of me feels it might actually be money well spent if Tripplehorn can be persuaded that there are more positive ways to motivate a choir to greater heights of musical excellence than to liken the sound made by the sopranos, as he had done this morning, to a pack of prairie dogs endeavouring to start a rusty Skoda.

Friday 9th May

Melvyn Samlesbury phoned me as I was getting home this evening to tell me he'd been delayed in heavy traffic. I really did hope to persuade him that he might prefer a bath and relaxing meal in his hotel rather than coming to join us for our rehearsal, but unfortunately he was quite insistent he wanted to attend, and hinted that he might even throw in an appraisal free of charge.

I did eventually strike a compromise deal with him, whereby he agreed to join us for the last forty minutes of the practice, with no appraisal. This in turn gave me sufficient time to go on ahead and warn my fellow choir members about his imminent arrival, thus enabling Tripplehorn to plan the rehearsal accordingly. I'm not sure whether I was relieved or disappointed that his absence from the first 50 minutes of the rehearsal deprived him of the sight of his lovingly-prepared masterpiece *Call To Remembrance*, dedicated to "my dear departed tortoise Aristotle, 16th November 1998," being hurled by Tripplehorn high into the air after our eleventh unsuccessful attempt to negotiate our way beyond page one.

We fared slightly better with his exuberant *Make A Joyful Noise*, composed, according to the title page, "on hearing of the recovery of Anthony from shingles, 1st February 1996," although our success may have been chiefly attributable to the fact that the work was in unison throughout with the organ playing the melody underneath. Tripplehorn made no secret of the fact that he wanted rehearsal of Melvyn's work out of the way before he arrived, and indeed we were well into Sunday's music when he joined us shortly before eight thirty. At ten to nine, having completed Sunday's work, Tripplehorn said "Right, let's call it a day now. You've sung very well tonight and you're all looking tired."

At once, Melvyn sprang up. "Forgive me," he said, "but I was looking forward to hearing you practise a few of my pieces for tomorrow. We really don't want to spend any time tomorrow note-bashing. Allow me to take the choir for a second or two. I promise I shan't keep you more than fifteen minutes."

Clearly, however, fifteen Lancastrian minutes did not have the same meaning as fifteen minutes in St Basil's. After 25 minutes by my watch, Tripplehorn had disappeared into the vestry, muttering about the need to do some urgent cleaning behind the cassock cupboard. Arthur Ramsbottom was poised to rewrite the last part of his choir history by reporting, in his inimitable slumber-inducing style, the longest practice since Percy Luffington kept the second basses behind for an extra hour one October night in 1966 because their Crotch was not up to scratch. And Irving Cattermole had just remembered that he had a very sick aunt in Nempnett Thrubwell.

Still, we did make some useful headway with Melvyn's all too aptly-named *Through The Night Of Doubt And Sorrow,* composed "on a forlorn platform of a remote country railway halt, 13th March 1992." As Ken whispered to me, it's a shame his train didn't come in a great deal sooner.

Saturday 10th May

I am sure I wasn't the only one to make my way to St Basil's this morning with some apprehension as to what lay ahead. But with most of the choir having signed up to Melvyn Samlesbury's workshop, and agreement having been reached by the PCC to subsidise his travelling costs, we looked likely to make a reasonable profit on the day, so I decided that on that basis the day would not go down as a complete disaster.

That, however, was before we got properly started. The first hint of trouble was Melvyn's decision to spend the whole of the first session, from the start right up to the morning coffee break, on warm-up exercises. With Matthew and Zoe smirking in the front row, it was perhaps ill-advised to insist on our going through a succession of upward and downward scales to the syllable "loo" and, shortly after that, a sequence of arpeggios using the syllable "pee." Since Joan Trumpington's leg was due to be inspected by her GP, neurophysician, hypnotherapist and faith healer, not necessarily in that order, it seemed somewhat tactless of our guest conductor to insist on our leaping to our feet and performing a series of physical jerks that would not have been out of place in the PE syllabus at SAS training school. And was it really necessary for Melvyn to stride over to Eileen Crosby, whose neckbrace only came out last week following a recent minor operation, to assert that her attempts at shoulder-loosening, which he had insisted on our keeping going for a good ten minutes, reminded him of a cross between Mike Yarwood's Ted Heath impersonation and a chimpanzee shaking off an attack of marauding mosquitoes.

But if we thought coffee was to bring relief, we were sadly mistaken. Melvyn more or less ordered us to get our drink as soon as possible then come and listen to a short lecture from him about his rehearsal technique, founded, in his words, on the Zuithuizen Principle. At no stage did he trouble to tell us who Mr, or possibly Mrs Zuithuizen was, but he was quite clear on the underlying philosophy. "Perfectionism," said Melvyn. "Aiming for a performance that is perfect. By a ruthlessly focussed approach. Learning the notes before the rehearsal, and using the rehearsal to refine the piece until perfection is achieved. Stopping after each and every imperfection. Micromanaging, if you like. Let one thing go, you may as well let it all go." This agenda struck me as being somewhat overambitious for a Royal College Of Music masterclass, let alone for a provincial parish choir the best singing days of some of whom had been left behind with Chopper bikes, *Children's Hour*, and banks that answered the phone to customers rather than first diverting their calls via Islamabad. It was certainly enough to deter all our paying audience members from staying. Indeed I saw them both beating a hasty retreat before we'd sung a single note of any of Melvyn's pieces.

To our relief, Melvyn decided to put his perfectionistic principles into practice with the ostensibly straightforward unison anthem, *Make A Joyful Noise*, which we'd looked at last night. With two hours to go until lunch, it seemed reasonable to suppose that we would dispose of this one quite quickly then swiftly move on to other pieces. But not a bit of it. Every single note and nuance came in for detailed analysis, from the breath erroneously taken by one of the sopranos on bar two of page seven to the failure of the altos to decrescendo on page 6 until two bars rather than three bars before "con tutta la forza ma non animato" at the top of page 9. And that was when the trouble really started. "Do either of you two youngsters know what that means?" Melvyn asked, looking meaningfully at Matthew and Zoe.

Fortunately, perhaps, Matthew hadn't developed his reparteeing skills to the extent of replying that he had eaten a plateful of it at dinner last night. It was left to Lesley, whose opinion of Melvyn had plummeted faster than a downward express lift injected with amphetamines, to say to Alison with a giggle, "I think it means, 'despite all her forcefulness my mother's not a beast.'"

Melvyn, whose patience had been wearing decidedly thin, rounded on Lesley instantly. "If you want to treat this as one big joke, we won't bother carrying on," he snapped.

"Well, let me tell you something," Lesley replied. "Unless we get on to something else this afternoon, by a proper composer, I am not staying here a moment more after lunch. And I think that goes for the rest of us." The ensuing nods of agreement were as close as we'd come to doing anything in time with each other all morning.

Melvyn Samlesbury did not hesitate. He picked up his folder and walked straight out, merely announcing "I shall expect my full fee for the day" as he did so.

For all Tripplehorn's faults, I don't think I have ever been so relieved to see him back on the conductor's rostrum. He suggested that as we so rarely got the chance to perform the Prayer Book matins and evensong settings of the canticles, we spend the afternoon looking at some of the works of Stanford – a suggestion that was warmly received by those present. Having said that, I think at that stage we would all have warmed to a history of the evolution of road traffic by-laws in Basutoland. Following a delicious lunch, we got stuck into some of the evensong settings, and it really was lovely to sing a good tuneful piece without being stopped every ten seconds. Indeed, so carried away was Tripplehorn by having his own choir back that he was unwise enough to let Cora Willoughby-Smith loose on the solo at the start of Stanford's

Magnificat in G – probably the last time she'll ever be allowed to get away with it. Especially when her shrill top G provoked a minor panic amongst some visitors admiring the churchyard outside. But for my timely intervention, any one of the emergency services might have been alerted to the scene.

Sunday 11th May

I think we all enjoyed this morning's service; quite how Tripplehorn managed to wangle it so we got to sing one of Stanford's evensong settings – one that we'd looked at yesterday afternoon – during a morning mass, I'm not sure, but we certainly did it justice. The vicar kindly agreed to donate this morning's collection to the vestry fund on the strength of it, too.

As we were leaving this morning, I remarked to Tripplehorn, who was in an excellent mood, that he must be pleased to have seen the back of Melvyn Samlesbury.

"It's all a bit embarrassing, really," Tripplehorn replied. "I realised that it wasn't at a Royal School Of Church Music do that we met. It was on the way home from the do. Queuing for a takeaway coffee at Leigh Delamere Services."

I told him it was a shame he hadn't realised that until yesterday.

"Oh, I had," he said. "It was just after you'd booked him, as a matter of fact. But you seemed so keen on the idea, I didn't like to say anything."

Almost speechless with indignation, I asked him if he had heard of the Zuithuizen Principle, or indeed who Zuithuizen was.

"I checked him out on the Internet last night," he said. "After a lot of searching I finally traced him and found what his claim to fame is in Mr Samlesbury's part of the world."

"What's that?" I asked him.

"He runs an ironmongery in Charnock Richard," Tripplehorn replied.

Tuesday 13th May

The first week of four in which we have Tuesday as well as Friday choir practices in preparation for the Rogationtide walk on the 31st of this month and then singing the Pentecost services at Exeter Cathedral eight days after that. Happily today I at last confirmed the final arrangements with Crispin Peacock. Having decided that if we put on a choral matins we will be lucky to attract a congregation consisting of any more than a hard-of-hearing church mouse and half a dozen indolent death-watch beetles, we have opted simply for a lunchtime recital and an evensong, performing in just two churches instead of the original three. We will make our way by minibus or car to Everard-cum-Millicent, then using part of the route I took during my second exploratory walk in February, we will walk to Zoyland St Quentin. Here we will perform the lunchtime recital, then, again retracing my February steps, we will use a different route to return to Everard-cum-Millicent for evensong. The vicar of the two churches has promised to ensure us a full house at both events, with the congregations giving to a retiring collection in aid of the vestry fund. Following the evensong we are invited back for drinks and light supper at the home of Eric Littlejohn whom I'd met on my exploratory walk three months ago. After our experiences on Easter Monday, we've decided to dispense with any pub stop at all which means there's a considerable amount of planning needed for the lunchtime catering arrangements. Much of tonight's practice time was utilised discussing what picnic food we should take and who was to bring it – much to Tripplehorn's irritation, needless to say.

Tripplehorn has sensibly decided that some of the music we are doing at Exeter can also be sung for the evensong at Everard-cum-Millicent, which reduces the total workload a little, but as he said, a much higher standard will be expected of us in the cathedral. He reminded us of Anthony Cartwright's promise of a further financial contribution for *Spirit Of Fire* on it being premiered in the cathedral, for it is one of the aims of the trust fund that the musical profile of St Basil's extends into the wider world. This contribution has also been earmarked for the vestry fund, although judging by the mess we made of my piece when we looked at it tonight, I don't think Anthony Cartwright needs to get his chequebook out just yet. Predictably enough, Hazel Ledworthy, who had actually been quite helpful as far as promising to provide picnic food was concerned, complained about it the moment it was handed out, staring contemptuously at it as though it was something the cat had dragged in and then saying "Isn't there enough decent church music in the repertoire without our having to experiment with new works like this?" Then every time Tripplehorn commented adversely on a missed entry or mishit note, she tried to blame the printing of the piece, citing everything from the "absurd" font size used to print the words to the "disgraceful" layout of the music which permitted a jump from a D sharp at the end of page 6 to a G natural at the top of page 7. And by the time we were through, I as the editor now rejoiced in the honour of being credited with the IQ of a tailor's dummy and the practical common sense of an oven-ready hedgehog.

I'm actually quite surprised she's coming to the picnic. But I can't claim to be optimistic about her inviting me to poke my breadstick into her salsa dip.

Wednesday 14th May

Arthur Ramsbottom rang me as I was preparing supper this evening and told me that not only would the final section of his book be with me by Sunday but he had a "very exciting development" to report as far as its preparation for publication was concerned. Wondering for an insane moment if in fact his work had been accepted by one of the big London publishing houses, I instantly pictured in my mind's eye the queues of people all night down Piccadilly or Oxford Street waiting for him to make his appearance at a signing session at Hatchards or Selfridges; the managing directors of the big supermarket chains sitting well into the small hours discussing what discounts off the cover price of the book to offer in their stores; and holidaymakers, encouraged by the wealth of superlatives heaped upon it by even the most hardened and cynical newspaper reviewers, fighting with each other in the airport departure lounge bookstalls for the privilege of snapping up precious copies to while away their transatlantic flights or their hours on the sun-drenched Caribbean beaches.

These ludicrous visions faded and died as Arthur announced what the news actually was. "I've bought myself a typewriter," he told me. "Found one in the Oxfam shop this morning. In perfect working order. I can now type up the whole script for you."

I resisted the temptation to tell him I'd now stay up all night watching the satellite news channel in eager anticipation of an announcement that he'd managed to procure a new black and red typewriter ribbon as well. However I did tell him, in so many words, that as I had spent the equivalent of about five full working days deciphering his scribble in order to get it on to my PC, his news, welcome though it at first appeared, had come marginally too late.

"Well, never mind," Arthur prattled on. "I'm already planning the sequel. About what happened to former choir members after they left us. I'm sure other choir and church members would find it very entertaining. I'll drop round what I've done so far."

Just the thought of having to wade through any more of Arthur's mediocre musings beyond the choir history, whether typed or not, was sufficient to cast a cloud over my Aunt Dora's Kitchen Individual Chicken and Asparagus Pie and Savemart Morning Fresh Frozen Peas. And the preliminary sample material, delivered by him within half an hour of our telephone conversation, did little to allay my misgivings about the viability of this latest project. Many readers would I am sure be both surprised and delighted to note that Andrew Cresswell (treble, 1965-1970) had gone on to become a well-established lay clerk in one of the principal cathedral choirs in the North of England. It is altogether less certain how interested any potential purchasers will be in the fortunes of

Ernest Penkethman (bass, 1950-1973) whose only reward for twenty three years' unstinting devotion to the musical aspect of the worship at St Basil's appears to have been a subsequent appointment as acting deputy treasurer of the Penmaenmawr Parochial Church Council Churchyard and Church Outbuildings Maintenance Subcommittee.

Friday 16th May

A really good day today. Met Katie at lunchtime and we booked up a last-minute holiday in Prague, flying out next Friday evening and returning the following Wednesday. It'll be the first choir practice I've missed this year. At tonight's rehearsal I couldn't resist asking Arthur Ramsbottom if with the final material that was coming to me on Sunday there would be any statistics on unbroken sequences of choir practice or Sunday morning service attendance, as I was confident I might have beaten it. Obviously I was only joking, but before I got the chance to tell him so I was being advised that I had a way to go as Ernest Penkethman, no doubt now enjoying the Freedom of Penmaenmawr for his outstanding services to churchyard maintenance, put together a run of 486 successive practices, succumbing only on New Year's Eve 1971 owing to a painful bunion on the ball of his left foot.

And there was I thinking I'd never missed an episode of Roy Castle's *Record Breakers*.

After an excellent evening's sing, with some very good work done on my anthem, we spent further time tonight discussing the logistics of the Rogationtide walk. I was able to provide copies of the proposed route, and not entirely to my surprise there were one or two less than positive comments.

"Whatever the plan is," said Cora Willoughby-Smith, "I really don't want to be walking through any fields of cattle. Cows can be extremely inquisitive creatures and bulls downright dangerous. I remember...."

"At least bulls are quite clumsy," said Alison Sparkes. "I have a problem with dogs. The smaller they are, the nastier and more lethal they can be. I don't mind...."

"Sheep are just as bad," Eileen Crosby lamented. "They look innocent and cuddly enough. But some can be just as aggressive as dogs. In fact...."

"It's not so much the fields or the animals I mind," Craig Dumbleton put in. "It's woodland and forest. Very claustrophobic and so easy to get lost. You spend hours walking along a woodland path and then it fades into nothing and you forget how you got there in the first place. I remember doing a railway walk on the old Somerset and Dorset a few years back...."

"Let's get one thing absolutely clear," barked Hazel Ledworthy. "If this walk involves the climbing of any stiles, I refuse to be part of it. Especially after what happened last…."

"Never mind that," Irving Cattermole cut in. "I insist on proper catering. I really don't see, after working up an appetite, I should be forced to endure having to perch on a groundsheet chewing on half-squashed pork pies and drinking lukewarm tea with bits of thermos flask floating on the top of it."

Which brought us to the vexed question of the amount of equipment that we'll have to take with us, which includes not only a Fortnum & Mason hamper for Irving Cattermole and sufficient picnic food for the rest of us, but also music and choir robes. There were further dark murmurings about the health and safety consequences, not to mention the effect upon our musical performance, of having to carry it all on our backs.

"There's no problem there," Tripplehorn said. "We've a minibus that's going to transport all of that. It'll meet us at Zoyland St Quentin and we simply collect our robes and lunches from there when we arrive."

"Who's organising the bus?" Brian Ellis enquired.

"I am," said Joan Trumpington.

It's all a bit like that skit on the British Airways ad. Concert at St Cuthbert's. Service at St Saviour's. And vestments in Vancouver.

Sunday 18th May

At church this morning, Arthur Ramsbottom provided me with the final – typed – chapter of his book. "Do look after it," he said to me. "A great deal of very hard work has gone into it. It has meant so much to me." He sounded as though he was entrusting me with a priceless family heirloom. My hope for a new typewriter ribbon was sadly misplaced; furthermore, the keys had smacked so hard against the page that almost every "o" had a hole through the middle of it, and every capital letter was a good centimetre or so above the line. It reminded me rather of my visit with Katie to the town museum a month or so ago and its exhibition of typed correspondence of the pre-war years. Though I cannot recall its exact content, I'm quite sure that set against Arthur's prose I detected more humour, perceptiveness and inspiration in the response by Medmerry's High Class Grocery to the August 1935 enquiry of Mr P.F. Bloomer as to when they were expecting the next delivery of calves' foot jelly.

Since I guessed the final chapter was likely to include events that had taken place after I had joined the choir, I turned to the last couple of pages. The first thing I noticed was a hideously sycophantic pen-picture of Frank Tripplehorn, described as "an inspirational leader with sufficient vision to carry the St Basil's choir well into the new minnellium." (sic) Cora was diplomatically labelled as a "leading light and high profile figure, always at the cutting edge of choir life," and Hazel Ledworthy was euphemistically given the accolade of "loyal, stalwart member, never afraid to speak candidly about pertinent issues." I was moderately gratified to find myself referred to as a "real asset" to the tenor section, but moderately horrified at the thought of being seen by Arthur as "part of a vocal line that will swell the ranks of the heavenly congregation on the eternal feast day of the Lord." The thought of spending eternity sandwiched between Arthur Ramsbottom, singing everything con belto and unblendabilissimo, and Craig Dumbleton, haranguing me about signalling problems at Beckenham Junction, was so ghastly that it failed to register with me at the time that Arthur had provided some supplemental material, pursuant to my ill-advised enquiry on Friday evening. Later, at home, I found this material to consist of pages of statistical information, including the names and dates of office of all the choirmasters, an alphabetical list of all known choir members, and a "summary of red-letter days in the choir history" such as the year rehearsals were moved from Thursday nights to Friday nights, the year fines for non-attendance at rehearsal were abolished, and the year the old black robes were discarded for the present light blue ones. Incredibly, Arthur was suggesting that anyone spotting an inaccuracy in this section, or wishing to add to it, should contact him "so that appropriate amendments can be made for the next edition." Which presumably will appear when and only when the first one is sold out. I suppose there may be people around in the year 2150 who will heave a sigh of relief when it is confirmed for the avoidance of doubt that it was definitely 1974 and not 1973 when it ceased to be compulsory for boy trebles to wear ruffs round their necks. And who will pity their poor forebears of five generations ago for being under the sad misapprehension that it was 1968, rather than the correct 1969, that the organ was first treated for leather fatigue.

Tuesday 20th May

Now that I have the complete script of the choir history, the pressure really is on to engage the services of a firm which will get the book properly bound and printed. At choir tonight Tripplehorn was able to confirm the amount of money the PCC are prepared to offer up front to finance the job; not surprisingly it isn't a huge sum, as there's no guarantee they'll get any of it back. I asked him if he knew of any local printer who would do a reasonably quick and inexpensive job. "Give Tony Smart a call," he said. "He's our resident computer expert and he's done quite a lot of printing for me. If he can't do it, he'll quickly point you in the direction of someone who can."

Mindful that I'm away for most of the rest of this month, I took advantage of his grilling the sopranos and altos on the one women-only anthem we're to sing at Zoyland St Quentin in eleven days to ring Tony straight away. He kindly agreed to meet me in the pub straight after the practice, asking if I could bring with me the work I'd already done so he would have some idea of the length and layout.

I did vaguely know Tony; he had helped me to get my own PC up and running last February, and from what I had seen and heard from others, he seemed to possess the rare combination of real Christian compassion with a quirky and sometimes mischievous sense of humour, as though part of him had never really grown up. To avoid bumping into Arthur Ramsbottom we decided to meet at the Three Horseshoes rather than the choir's usual pub, and over a glass of whisky he read snatches at random. After the first snatch he was grinning. After the third snatch the grin had broadened into a beaming smile. Five snatches later he was in stitches of hysterical laughter.

"I know just the firm for this," he said, after wiping the last tears of merriment from his eyes. "They charge very reasonably indeed and for the print run you have in mind can turn the whole job around in less time than it takes to tell. I've used them often and they've never let me down. They're called Cramp and Sons, at the end of Wallwork Road. Give them a call."

I was touched by Tony's obvious concern for the success of the project and his evident enthusiasm about the material he had seen, and it was with a sense of new-found optimism that I left him, pleased that my evening had been productively utilised and that Arthur's project, into which so much hard work had gone, would soon be generating cash for such a worthy cause.

Drove down Wallwork Road on the way home and found Cramp and Sons. A firm of private waste disposal contractors.

Thursday 22nd May

Having reflected further on Tony's reaction to Arthur's book, I rang Tripplehorn this morning intending to tell him that in all conscience I just didn't think it right to ask the PCC for the money for the binding and printing and that accordingly we should scrap the whole scheme. "Funny you should ring," he said. "I've just been on the Internet in search of a local printer for a separate job of my own. I've found one here that may interest you. Extremely competitively priced, all-singing, all-dancing. I'll give you their website address."

I looked it up straight away. The name of the firm is Quick Print, and indeed they do offer a very comprehensive service which includes allocation of ISBN, cover design including the insertion of a barcode, printing, binding and delivery. Some sample prices were given, and I was delighted to see that for the number of copies I want the bill is going to be much lower than I feared, and even if not a single copy was sold the loss would not be too great for the PCC. A quick phone call back to Tripplehorn confirmed I could go ahead on the basis of the price quoted.

Was slightly concerned that there appeared to be no postal address, no contact name and no landline quoted on the website; the only contact detail consisted of a mobile phone number which if I tried once I tried twenty times. Finally, just before lunch, the phone was answered with a gruff "Hallo" and a few moments later I found myself in conversation with the manager of Quick Print. He was good enough to inform me that his name was Malcolm, but he seemed as coy about revealing his surname as he was about disclosing his address and landline number on his website. Judging by the background noise I could hear at his end, I couldn't work out if he was driving a ten-ton lorry through the Dartford Tunnel or sitting watching his smalls being deep-fried in the Park Road Launderama. But, persevering hard, I explained my project then turned to my carefully-prepared list of questions.

"Would you be able to print, bind and deliver 200 copies of a 164 page book by the end of October?" I asked him.

"Yeah, no probs," he replied.

"And you'll be able to send me a formal quote and contract within 7 days, is that right?"

"Yeah, no difficulties," he replied.

"Am I right in thinking that by simply emailing the typeset text to you, you can print direct from my copy?"

"Yeah, no sweat," he replied.

"And can I confirm that there's no need for payment up front but you'll invoice me when the job is done?"

"Yeah, no worries," he replied.

"And you'll supply the ISBN?"

"Yeah, no trouble," he replied.

"And I gather that if I tell you the cover specifications, you can deal with that too?"

There was a pause, presumably for him to consult his thesaurus. "Yeah, no hassles," he said.

Moments later, each of my outstanding issues surrounding the project succinctly and positively dealt with, I hung up. With all the confidence and peace of mind of a three-legged warthog called upon to perform a tap dance number at the Amazonian Anaconda Confederation's annual summer ball.

Friday 30th May

A nice start to the practice, as Matthew, whose mum can't join us for our expedition tomorrow, told me he would donate his week's pocket money to the vestry fund if I will allow him to map read on the walk. Apparently it's related to a geography project he's doing at school. I was happy to agree, on the basis that I would come to his rescue if he threatened to lead us, accidentally or on purpose, into any cattle sheds, bull-infested fields, or maximum security defence establishments.

A longer than usual practice tonight, going through the music for tomorrow's marathon. Not that I was in any position to complain, having missed Tuesday's rehearsal as a result of what had been a lovely holiday with Katie. At the end of the rehearsal I mentioned that it would be good to see family and friends of choir members at one of the churches tomorrow at least, to show their support and possibly contribute to the collections.

"Well, I'm sorry," said Irving Cattermole. "And this is no criticism of you whatsoever, because I know you're doing your best, but I think it's unreasonable to expect the same people to keep sponsoring or supporting us all the time." Not that I think he has invited any friend or family member to a single event, but never mind.

"I did try to ask one or two people if they'd come," Craig Dumbleton lamented, "but they told me they're involved in another big fundraising event in town tomorrow and I can't really ask them to do both."

"What event?" I asked, groaning inwardly. There were so many people whose need was far more desperate than ours, and for whom fund raising was a bigger priority, barely a stone's throw from our church lychgate. Down-and-outs camping out on our streets in all weathers. The mentally handicapped, deprived of proper day care. The elderly and infirm, unable even to perform many of the basic functions in life which the able-bodied took for granted. The blind and partially sighted, who only last week had lost their local talking newspaper service.....

"It's the bring-and-buy in the town hall for the St Leodegar's School Minibus Appeal," said Henry. "Giving the children access to learning opportunities outside the immediate catchment area."

"Oh, come off it," said Alison Sparkes. "That school has got about ten minibuses already. There's enough petrol-guzzling machines there to triple carbon dioxide levels across the whole of southern England in the next five years."

"Yes, but our children's education is at stake here," said Henry Peasgood. "Would be far more educational if they actually stayed in the classroom and did some sums," Irving Cattermole commented. And within minutes, just about the whole choir had become embroiled in a quite heated discussion. At least it redirected Irving Cattermole's vitriol away from me and on to the shortcomings of the teaching profession in general and St Leodegar's School's policies on matters appertaining to pollution control in particular. But it still wasn't helping my cause, and frankly the last thing I wanted, with dinner at Katie's beckoning tonight and a long day ahead tomorrow, was a three-hour debate on the educational value of twice-termly outings to Madame Tussaud's Waxworks, Beaulieu Motor Museum or, for that matter, the Chipping Sodbury Centre of East Paraguayan Abstract Raffia Design.

Saturday 31st May

A nice easy ride in our support vehicle, donated to us for the day by one of the churchwardens, to Everard-cum-Millicent. We were blessed with a fine sunny morning, the heat tempered by a fresh south-westerly breeze. Perfect walking weather in fact. It was therefore a shame that presumably on the strength of this morning's shipping forecast, which had reported a light shower just off German Bight and moderate precipitation twenty miles from Rockall, there was a sudden outbreak of cold feet amongst a number of those who had promised to undertake the walk. By the time the waverers had made up their minds one way or the other, the only ramblers remaining appeared to be myself, Craig Dumbleton, Matthew Sparkes and Henry Peasgood. Still feeling irritable after the late finish last night, I said quite snappishly "Oh, for heaven's sake. Is there really nobody else who's prepared to walk?" Somewhat to my surprise, this appeal did elicit a response, from Cora Willoughby-Smith's sister Josephine. The five of us set off on foot towards Zoyland St Quentin, while the others stayed with the bus which was also conveying our robes and refreshment.

Progress was initially excellent, but became fitful and after four hundred yards Josephine complained that her shoes were rubbing and asked if she had time to hurry back to the support vehicle and put on a different pair. Already I was beginning to have regrets about my impassioned appeal for more walkers. Regrets which rapidly turned into exasperation when another three hundred yards further on, she decided that her first pair of shoes were actually more comfortable after all. I did suggest, after her second journey back to the bus, that it might be prudent for her to keep both pairs of shoes with her in future: a suggestion which I was only too pleased to have made following further changes of footwear at the first fence, the canal turn, the eight furlong mark and the water jump.

The upshot was that even though Matthew's map reading was excellent – my recollection of the route wasn't as clear as I'd have liked, so his assistance actually proved extremely helpful – we reached Zoyland St Quentin very late, and found ourselves in the embarrassing position of having to start the recital a full 35 minutes behind schedule. There was a reasonable but far from spectacular turnout, and indeed there appeared to be to be more noise and activity outside than in. This seemed to intensify as we worked our way through one of the more challenging pieces of the day, Byrd's *Ave Verum*. During one of the strategic pauses in the middle of the work, the vicar of the church suddenly rose from his seat and announced "Thank you very much, choir of St Basil's. Now, if I could ask you as quickly as possible to vacate your seats to allow the wedding party to enter."

"I beg your pardon," said Tripplehorn, "but we have another four pieces to do. Four and a half to be precise. We haven't actually finished this one yet."

"Well, I'm sorry," said the vicar. "If you had started on time you'd be out by now. And this wedding has been booked for the last fifteen months. Can you please leave. I'll take the retiring collection and see you before you go."

We did manage to negotiate with the vicar to the extent of at least being allowed to finish the piece we were halfway through singing, but to the accompaniment of the vanguard of the wedding party making their way noisily and messily into the church. We duly trooped out, Tripplehorn telling Lesley that even if it killed him he would somehow incorporate all the unsung pieces into the evensong service later, and I asked everyone to gather round so the vicar could give us the collection money and I could explain where we were meeting for our picnic.

A few moments later Matthew, who I noticed hadn't filed out with us, reappeared, clutching a paper bag full of banknotes and coins.

"Where have you been? And where on earth did you get all that lot from?" Lesley asked him.

"Oh, I had a whip-round amongst the wedding guests waiting outside," he said. "Told all the wedding party what a fantastic cause they were giving to. Come on, I'm starving." Having said which, he thrust the money into my hands and sped off towards the field which I'd told him marked the start of the next stage of the walk that would take us to our picnic spot near Wetherford.

Couldn't help thinking it was somewhat ironic that we had generated far more money from our singing here than we would have been likely to get had we turned up on time and been allowed by the vicar to finish the programme.

I offloaded the money on to Tripplehorn, and was about to set off with the rest of the walking party in pursuit of Matthew. Before I could go, however, the vicar said "Word of warning. If you're heading for Wetherford, don't try and cross Beggar's Bridge. It's unsafe."

Unfortunately the warning came too late. Despite sprinting across the adjacent field, leaving the other walkers trailing in my wake, I was just in time to see Matthew execute a series of elaborate bodily manoeuvres which would have been a credit to the Russian Olympic gymnastics team and, with a blood-curdling cry and an ear-splitting splash, fall head first into the River Ubblesbourne. Fortunately the flow was reasonably light, following a dry spring, and the river was narrow enough a couple of hundred yards upstream for the rest of us to jump across, but it was still with a heavy heart that I surveyed the damage once my fellow walkers and I had pulled Matthew to his feet. Rivulets of fluid coursed down the front of his T-shirt and his trousers, while the whole of his clothing was now caked in an unappetising rich brown and even less alluring stench as befitted river water that had just flowed through the regional works of the West Shires Sewage Company.

No doubt motivated by the fear of missing his picnic lunch, Matthew insisted that we all carried on to the picnic site which fortunately was only another twenty minutes' walk away, and proceeded to down not only all of his share of the sandwiches, but the portions of those for whom the odour of human and animal effluent was too much to contemplate any solid refreshment at all. It was only after he had finished off two cartons of Ribena and four fun-size Mars Bars that Tripplehorn insisted he returned him home at once to get bathed and changed, even though it would mean driving the bus all the way there and back. Other logistically complex options were considered, but because time was now so short there was no other realistic possibility, even though bus travellers would therefore be deprived of the opportunity to visit the Woodturners' and Pipemenders' Workshop in the nearby village of Camelsfoot Under Lizard. Fortunately no insurrection ensued from those deprived of this cultural bonanza and the bus was soon on its way, Joan Trumpington having volunteered to navigate. It did strike me that this was rather like entrusting the management of Stringfellows to the Mother Superior of the Trappist convent of the Madonna of the Seven Hills, Mount Chimborazo, and it was no surprise to me when the bus set off, amid a cloud of dust and smoke, in what was obviously the wrong direction. Taking Matthew, and my precious map, with it.

Nevertheless, I had planned and walked the route and was optimistic that I could remember it without the aid of the map. We started confidently enough, and I was actually beginning to enjoy the walk when we arrived at a gate that was securely padlocked with no possibility of getting round the obstruction and, without the map, no means of knowing where we had gone wrong. To make matters worse, it was totally impossible to get a signal on my mobile phone through which I might somehow have got some assistance. It was agreed that the best thing to do was to cut our losses, find the shortest way back to Zoyland St Quentin and then use roads to get back to Everard-cum-Millicent, hiring a fleet of taxis if necessary.

Fortunately, Josephine reminded us that about half an hour ago we had crossed a road, and she was pretty sure she remembered seeing a nearby signpost with Zoyland St Quentin mentioned on it. Accordingly, we agreed to backtrack. Although I didn't remember crossing quite so much barbed wire or crawling under any electric fences first time, we did hit the road which happily led back to Zoyland St Quentin and even more happily the pub here was able to provide the numbers of two taxi firms and also a payphone.

The only problem being that it was now ten past five and evensong had been scheduled for five o'clock.

At five fifty we arrived back in Everard-cum-Millicent, expecting to see an irate Tripplehorn storming out of the church having been forced to run the evensong service with only half the choir membership. Instead of which, a tentative glance through the door of the church revealed a congregation and clergy of precisely zero, and not a St Basil's choir member or choirmaster in sight. We went back outside, and almost immediately we saw the bus drawing up outside the church, and, simultaneously, the vicar hurrying up towards us.

"Oh, there you are," he said. "We were all waiting for you. A packed church it was. What happened?"

Tripplehorn exited from the bus and muttered a few ill-chosen words about incompetent navigators directing buses straight into the path of speeding farm tractors, and mothers of sewage-soaked trebles going AWOL necessitating search parties across a radius of five miles in order to locate house keys.

"Still, never mind," said the vicar. "We made the best of a bad job. One of my churchwardens has just given us a superb slide show about his holiday on the Inca Trail. Tremendous it was. Of course we had to donate the retiring collection to him and not to you. But I can tell you it was a very good cause."

"What cause?" I enquired.

"The St Leodegar's School Minibus Appeal," said the vicar.

JUNE

Sunday 1st June – *SUNDAY AFTER ASCENSION DAY*

Following a long but most agreeable evening at Eric Littlejohn's house – he had attended the lunchtime recital so I didn't feel too bad about accepting his hospitality despite the evensong debacle – it was quite an effort to drag ourselves to church for this morning's service. We were faced with another quite hefty menu of music, as we had decided not to sing on Ascension Day itself but were celebrating Ascensiontide today; with yesterday and Exeter to prepare for, Tripplehorn felt yet another service with choir involvement was excessive. The vicar came up to us before the service and said "I do hope you'll do the Ascension music justice this morning. One or two members of the congregation are rather upset that there was no sung celebration on the proper day. They do feel that this moving of celebration of the Christian feasts undermines the subtle pattern of the church's year." Irving Cattermole fortunately waited till the vicar had moved out of earshot before observing that if the demeanour, age and state of mental health of most of the congregation was anything to go by, most would not notice if the liturgy for Harvest Thanksgiving was moved to the third Tuesday before the Russian Orthodox Easter.

The singing this morning was tired and I think we were all grateful for the cancellation of Tuesday's practice, although Tripplehorn warned us that to make up for that we may need a longer rehearsal in the stalls in Exeter next Sunday afternoon. "Will kill two birds with one stone, anyway," he said to me afterwards. "I'm sure most of the clergy there are excellent, but every time I've done a service there I've had to put up with doddery precentors and celebrants and have had to go through everything with them chapter and verse. At least if I can get next Sunday's geriatric to come and join us for even part of the practice, there's just a chance the service will run as it's supposed to."

Somewhat alarmed at the implication that my anthem might be either announced halfway through the intercessions or inserted into the pre-service trailers and commercials, and more to reassure myself than anything else, I told him I was sure that with higher standards these days, the risk of disaster was greatly reduced.

"Oh, they're switched on enough at times," said Tripplehorn. "A friend of mine was once in Exeter and heard the most clueless precentor of the lot, Cedric Loxley, intone each of the evensong collects quite beautifully, and in tune. His two hundred listeners, each of whom heard every word, were spellbound." He paused to fling a heap of music into the cupboard. "It was just a shame that the listeners in question were in the Alexandra

Hotel attending the annual dinner of the South Devon Guild Of Laundrymen And Dry Cleaners."

Friday 6th June

Final rehearsal at church tonight for the performance of my anthem at Exeter. Mike Pitheavlis, who is to play the organ for us on Sunday, joined us tonight, and it was quite heart-warming to hear him say how much he liked my work.

For the second Friday practice in a row we found ourselves discussing travelling arrangements for the weekend, though fortunately this time the whole plan is rather simpler. Because we are taking several of our clergy and congregation with us, we have hired a coach for the trip to Exeter. The coach company, booked through Margaret Pardew, specialises in value-for-money transport for church groups and is said to offer "Christian standards of driver civility, comfort and customer care" – the latter reflected, one supposes, in the somewhat conservative choices of in-coach video films that are on offer to us on the day.

It was quite exciting to see the schedule of services for the next week at Exeter Cathedral including, against Pentecost Sunday 8th June, the magic words "Evensong sung today by the choir of St Basil." The list of music was also set out, and I was delighted to see my name as the composer of the anthem. It was just a bit disappointing that they'd printed out the anthem title as *Spirit Off Ire*. Trust Henry Peasgood to be the one to draw attention to it. But Brian, bless his heart, seeing my discomfiture, nobly chipped in. "Reminds me of my first ever lead role in a Gilbert and Sullivan opera," he said. "The programme missed off the first letter of the last word of my character and turned me into the Duke of unstable."

It did set me thinking that as a game to occupy us in the coach on the way down, and an improvement on the rather dismal entertainment the coach company have in mind for us, we could think of other similar typing errors that would produce amusing anthem titles, with a prize for the most imaginative. What I suppose I should have bargained for was the eagerness with which choir members began to conceive their own allegedly rib-tickling plays on words during this evening's practice. Lesley speculated that those involved in price wars in the town's fish shops might sing "Dearer my cod to thee," Brian said that someone released without charge after intensive police questioning might "Rejoice in the law doorway" and Alison remarked that jostling on Noah's Ark might produce "Shoving leopard of thy sheep." By the time Matthew had reminded us of the stingy McDonald's meal in which "I saw three chips" I was actually positively salivating with anticipation of the coach company's menu of on-board delights. In fact, I doubt if I'll get much sleep tomorrow night at the enthralling prospect of instruction on goat husbandry in Africa and the development of the dried flower industry in Droitwich.

Pentecost Sunday 8th June

Quite a novelty to have a Sunday morning off from choir duty today but Tripplehorn was most anxious that we should set off in time to allow us to have a picnic lunch and then a good full afternoon's rehearsal.

No problems to begin with. The coach was ten minutes early and a headcount confirmed that we were all present and correct a full five minutes before the advertised departure time. We all agreed we might as well make a start.

"Well, thank heaven for small mercies," Lesley remarked, glancing in Arthur Ramsbottom's direction as the coach headed out of town. "At least that annoying little man's not going round waving his wretched camcorder at everybody within ten paces."

At the mention of the word "camcorder" Arthur gave an involuntary start. "Oh, my goodness," he said, "I've quite forgotten to bring it with me. I knew I was forgetting something." Before Lesley could react, he had hurtled down the aisle of the coach and was asking the driver to make an unscheduled diversion. The driver, no doubt in adherence to his company's Christian standards of comfort and customer care, agreed to oblige, and moments later was weaving between double-parked cars on Smithfield Drive. Less in accordance with the biblical principles underpinning the ethos of his company was his language as he struggled to manoeuvre around a carelessly parked builders' van and was then forced to brake hard to avoid squashing a young girl who had careered out into the middle of the road on a lime green tricycle.

Still, the delay was not serious and we were more or less back to schedule as we came on to the M5 twenty five minutes later, only to go slap into a wall of solid traffic. Cue another round of expletives from our chauffeur, which stretched the concept of Christian standards of driver civility beyond that which even the most liberal theologians would have regarded as morally permissible. He pointed out to us that had he not been preoccupied with the Smithfield Drive diversion he would have caught the last half-hourly travel bulletin which would have warned of the hold-up and he could have avoided the M5 altogether. Now there was no way back, and another travel bulletin five minutes or so later confirmed the worst. There had just been an accident two junctions ahead of us involving a lorry shedding bottles of perfume, deodorant and haircare products all over the westbound carriageways. Inevitably, cars swerving to avoid an onslaught of Extra Dry Sure and Head And Shoulders Shampoo had crashed into each other and generated an instant pile-up. Fortunately it seemed nobody had been hurt. The radio announcer, secure in his studio, was thoroughly enjoying himself, mentioning that anybody trying to travel westwards on the M5 this morning would be "more than a little lacquered" but somehow the joke seemed to lose its potential to amuse after six separate renditions or variations on same. It wasn't until another hour had passed that we actually began to move, only to reach the next junction and find ourselves diverted off the motorway altogether. The diversionary route took us fifteen miles out of our way along intolerably slow roads, and in the space of nine miles we were overtaken by at least eight cyclists and, at one point, by a couple of elderly joggers. Still, thanks to the eagerly-awaited coach video spectacular, I now consider myself to be a real expert on the seasonal variation in milk yields of the North Liberian angora.

We arrived at Exeter with just an hour and a half to spare before the service was due to start. I think Tripplehorn would have been quite happy to press on with the rehearsal in the cathedral at once, but we were all so shattered by the long journey that he reluctantly agreed we could have half an hour's break before meeting in the song school and from there processing to the stalls in our robes for a very brief rehearsal. It seemed a rather ambitious timescale, particularly when we saw at least two of our number join a lengthy queue for a table in the nearby Pizza Hut, although their evident hunger was understandable in view of the events of the morning. Katie and I found a delightful pavement café and enjoyed some soup and crusty bread, then returned to the song school, making it seconds before the agreed meeting time.

On arrival, we found Tripplehorn in a rage. "Half the choir still aren't here, and there are no hymn books and no orders of service," he stormed. "Are all the choirs that come here supposed to sing the whole blasted service off by heart?" With scant regard for the tidiness of the song school, he began feverishly hurling heaps of music and other books to one side in search of the missing articles, until it was pointed out that their most likely home was in a cupboard labelled VISITING CHOIR HYMN BOOKS AND ORDERS OF SERVICE. Tripplehorn grabbed the handle of the cupboard door and yanked it, only for it to come away in his hand; now in a virtual frenzy, he seized the nearest sharp object and attempted to use it to prise open the cupboard door. All the time he was doing this, he was following our driver's lead and letting out a torrent of vehement invective which would have been barely acceptable to the censors of post-watershed Friday night Channel 4, never mind within the medieval walls of an ecclesiastical song school. The main gist of his Anglo-Saxon tirade was that there would be no time whatsoever to rehearse properly in the stalls or to go through the music with today's precentor, Harold Potteridge, who he said boasted the brain the size of a "thyroid-deficient anorexic stick insect."

Unfortunately, his somewhat amateurish efforts at breaking and entering, and his none too complimentary comments about the presiding clergyman, were witnessed by a green-robed member of the cathedral staff who had come in, unnoticed by him, a moment before. Politely he came up to our choirmaster and in a surprisingly kindly voice asked him if he would mind awfully not exerting quite so much brute force on the song school's fixtures and fittings. Most visiting choir leaders, anxious to make a good impression, would have apologised profusely, but the expression "When you're in a hole stop digging" is not part of the Tripplehorn Book Of Worldly Wisdom, and he compounded our discomfiture by retorting "If your staff had an ounce of common sense between them, they'd have remembered to open up the cupboard and get the service books and hymn books out for us beforehand."

"That's precisely what we've done," said the green robe, pointing to a heap of books on a side shelf which Joan Trumpington had effectively been masking for the past fifteen minutes.

The upshot of it was that by the time the latecomers had returned from lunch and everyone had been equipped with hymn books and service sheets, there was no time either to rehearse in the stalls or to go through the order of service with Potteridge, who was also leading the worship. Consequently, we began the service in an atmosphere that was tense to say the very least. Nonetheless, I was looking forward to singing my anthem, as was Anthony Cartwright who had travelled specially from home to Exeter for the occasion. But my hopes were dashed when Potteridge, having previously intoned the responses instead of the preces and announced the Te Deum instead of the Magnificat, failed to announce the anthem at all and went straight on into the intercessions after his unbelievably tedious sermon – the most interesting and theologically challenging aspect of which had been his invitation to us all to partake of tea and cake in the refectory immediately afterwards. There was no possibility of inserting the anthem after the ensuing intercessions, for he then proceeded to announce the recessional hymn and before we knew it, the army of clergy and acolytes were lining up for their curtain call and sweeping us away with them.

To his credit, Tripplehorn recognised my bitter disappointment, and perhaps felt more than a twinge of guilt that his failure to liaise with Potteridge before the service had led to the anthem being overlooked. More to the point, perhaps, he was concerned about not getting the balance of Anthony Cartwright's money. Accordingly, the moment the vestry prayer had been uttered, he said "Right. Everybody into the stalls now. We're going to do *Spirit Of Fire* if it kills us." Brushing aside the protests of an elderly verger, he all but frogmarched us back into the stalls, in no particular order and certainly not with the meticulous decorum that had marked our earlier procession, then repaired briskly to the organ loft where he ordered Mike to stop playing the voluntary and to turn up *Spirit Of Fire* forthwith. Although it wasn't technically perfect, it went better than I could have dared to hope. What pleased me most was how its effectiveness in performance was enhanced by the cathedral acoustic.

It was only a shame that there was nobody there to listen to it.

Now beside himself with anger, Tripplehorn led us, with barely more processional acumen than had been shown four minutes twenty eight seconds previously, out to the assembly area to be met by Anthony Cartwright, who was clutching his umbrella in one hand and an iced bun in the other. "Terribly sorry," he said. "I was just helping myself to the tea in the refectory. I didn't realise you were doing the anthem. Fancy doing it again?" But by now the elderly verger whose protests Tripplehorn had waved aside so contemptuously a few minutes back, and the green-robed official who had been the butt of his earlier caustic comments, were now favouring us with stares that would have struck fear into Arnold Schwarzenegger's Terminator on three Shredded Wheats, and we all felt it best to make as hasty a departure as was humanly possible. Leaving our chances of collecting the balance of Anthony Cartwright's money, or indeed ever singing in Exeter Cathedral again, probably terminally lacquered.

Wednesday 11th June

A planning meeting tonight for one of the major fundraising events of the year, the choir summer party on 26th July which is to be held at Cora's house. I was particularly keen for the meeting to finish by nine as there were two very good films on the telly, only one of which I would be able to pre-record. Fortunately, Ruth's idea of meetings, namely her talking at everyone in turn following which they agree to do exactly what she tells them, does ensure they don't last long, and it was just a case of waiting to be told what my duties were and then I would be free to go.

In previous years, the party has consisted of a "bring your own" supper and impromptu entertainment by the choir, but Ruth has in mind something rather more upmarket this time. It will consist of a buffet, which she is organising through a personal contact, and as far as the music is concerned, there will be a mixture of full choir items and some pieces performed by professional musicians, whose services Ruth has also managed to engage through personal friendship and acquaintance. There will be no individual acts by choir members and Tripplehorn will decide what we sing.

So far so good; I'm sure I'm not the only one who does not want to hear an assortment of both past and present choir members make fools of themselves, especially having overheard Arthur on the coach on Sunday evening saying he was being press-ganged into joining Miranda Cobbledick's occasional close harmony group the Load Of Old Cobblers to record a musical skit on the revised format for the back calculation of annuity benefits for British servicemen stationed in British Columbia. I was beginning to think that I had come out of all this rather lightly when Ruth announced that as the major money-spinner of the evening she wants us to organise an "auction of promises" whereby those present bid against each other for the promise of the supply of goods or services to them.

She turned to me and said "You're to do two things. First, get some decent items that people can bid for and take away on the night. About twenty will do. From my dealings with the chamber of commerce, the shopkeepers round town are pretty good about giving stuff away as long as they're thanked publicly. Five bottles of booze, tops, nothing with a supermarket label obviously. A pink cuddly toy's a nice touch and fills out the table a bit. But nothing that's too naff. Punters can spot makeweight prizes a mile off. And if we don't want to get sued, check the use by dates on any food items you're offered. That's the first thing. Second thing, you need to obtain some promises of services which local businesses and parishioners will supply free of charge. You know, like a free haircut at the George Road barbers, or an hour's computer tuition with Tony Smart. Again, we need about twenty. Make sure if there are conditions the suppliers tell you clearly what they are. Check carefully what, if any, time limits might apply, get a contact name so they can't turn round three months later and deny all knowledge, and get a true cost valuation so we've an idea of the appropriate price at which to start the bidding. Oh, and if you happen to be in Park Road don't bother asking for a free meal for two at the Happy House."

"Because there are too many strings attached?" I queried.

"No," she said. "The environmental health department of the local council are shutting them down next week."

Friday 13th June

Having heard nothing whatsoever from Malcolm in connection with the binding and printing of Arthur's book, I decided to bring things to a head today. Miraculously I got through to him straight away on his mobile. "You must be sidekick," he said to me. "I was just about to phone you to tell you I've prepared the quote and draft contract. I should be able to get it to you within half an hour." Astonishingly, within ninety minutes it had arrived on my PC.

The euphoria was slightly dampened by the fact that nowhere on the draft contract or covering letter was there a telephone number apart from a mobile, or an address apart from an email address, and my rights to go back on the deal once agreed were listed under the general heading YOU'RE RIGHT TO CANCEL. But then, I had not actually paid anything up front and thus had nothing to lose if Malcolm employed his own sidekick powers to do a disappearing act. And subsequent enquiries had not yielded any quotes that were anywhere near as competitive as Malcolm's. Accordingly, I decided I might as well go with it, and duly emailed Malcolm to that effect.

A good sing at choir tonight. Tripplehorn in an unusually benevolent mood, perhaps because he was hoping that as many as possible would be free to hear a London church choir, who are apparently extremely good, sing evensong in St Basil's next Saturday. I may well go along with Katie. I was hoping Ruth would be at choir tonight so she could give me a bit of support with regard to my request for promises for the auction which I felt I needed to start gathering in as soon as I could. But she cried off with a chest infection and I was left to take the initiative on my own. Rather as expected, a mixed response. Eileen Crosby's promise to bake and personally deliver to the highest bidder one of her special fruit cakes constituted an excellent start. Matthew's offer to babysit for an evening will I am sure be snapped up by the few attenders at the party that still have children under the age at which they can look after themselves providing the beneficiaries abide by the conditions attaching which include no nappy changing, a free run of the fridge, and the availability of a television set that offers access to all the Sky Sports channels. But Craig Dumbleton's pledge to recite his own version of *The Walrus And The Carpenter*, with funny voices where applicable, seemed somehow to be missing the point altogether.

Trinity Sunday 15th June

Following the huge disappointment at Exeter, Anthony Cartwright has, bless him, thrown us something of a lifeline. After church this morning he told us he has managed to persuade West Shires FM to record us doing *Spirit Of Fire* this Saturday afternoon. Once the recording is broadcast, he will provide the balance of the commission fee, which had of course been withheld as a result of our failure to perform the anthem within the cathedral service. That was the good news. The bad news is that we will need to stay on an extra half hour on Friday to rehearse, and will have to reserve the whole of Saturday afternoon as well, in case there are any technical problems. I was afraid that a number of choir members would be unavailable at such short notice but amazingly almost everyone does seem to be free, the only dissenting voice I heard being that of Irving Cattermole muttering about having arranged to spend the afternoon rubbing sandpaper into his waste pipes.

"When's the recording going out?" Lesley asked.

"It'll be on Doug Launchberry's Sunday breakfast show," Tripplehorn replied. "Now West Shires FM's only spiritual output of the week. Sandwiched in between the news, sport, travel, weather, commercials and Cliff Richard."

"Actually, I quite like Doug Launchberry," said Rachel. "Do you think he'll be there on Saturday afternoon? You know, for an interview with the composer?"

"I sincerely hope not," Tripplehorn replied. "I've not felt the same way about him after one of his guests told him she was very anxious to talk to him about her Damascus Road conversion and he told her that if she had a problem with it she should ring the district council."

"He's not exactly hot on the evensong canticle settings either," Ken Foulkes added. "I remember when the organist of St Stephen's came on and told him they had Dyson lined up for their trip to St Paul's Cathedral."

"What did he say?" I asked him.

"He told them he was surprised the cathedral didn't have a vacuum cleaner of their own," Ken replied.

Friday 20th June

A long choir practice tonight, with a lot of time spent perfecting *Spirit Of Fire* for tomorrow's recording. "Sooner we get it right tomorrow afternoon, sooner we can all get away," said Tripplehorn. Katie has promised to treat me to tea tomorrow after it's finished, but on the strength of Cora's cringe-making vibrato on page three and Henry's positively painful glissando halfway down page seven, I don't think she needs to make any special arrangements for the Cosy Nook Tea Gardens to reserve a table for us just yet.

Ruth Hartnell is clearly on a roll. She now wants us to start planning for the choir Christmas play and concert which is planned for two nights during the first week in December. At choir tonight she produced the script of the one-act play *See Amid The Little Town Of Bethlehem*, which she told me she hugely enjoyed last December when visiting friends in Bristol. Apparently it's all about the hilarious attempts of a number of choristers to organise a carol-singing party. This will form the first half of the evening, and after seasonal refreshment we will go on to sing a selection of carols in the second half. She's asked me to book the afternoon of 6th July in the church hall for auditions for the play. I can't think why she should want to go through the charade of auditions when she will have worked out exactly what everybody is doing, both on stage and off. From the main lead down to the person who turns up on the night in anticipation that there might be something that needs doing and having shown a couple of old biddies to their seats stands around looking as useful as a spare pudding at a weight-watchers' conference.

Saturday 21st June

A cloudless, fresh, sunny day. Ideal for a day out with Katie. I can understand her disappointment that, notwithstanding our agreement to meet for tea later in the afternoon, our walk and lunchtime drink in town should have to be cut short by the need to be at church at 2.30 to record *Spirit Of Fire*.

Not a good start to the afternoon. The recording team arrived very late, and having downed the second half of my pint of West Shires Special Brew considerably faster than was good for me, I found myself with an unexpected extra 45 minutes to recover. The engineer was unbelievably fussy and must have tried us in about twelve different positions before deciding where he would like us to stand, then spent what seemed an eternity fiddling with his recording equipment and trying about a dozen different spots for that as well. Why it should have proved so much more time-consuming to set up than the CD recording we'd done last November, I really cannot think. He kept reassuring us at regular intervals that "we'll be getting under way very shortly," until Irving Cattermole was heard to mumble "If that oaf says that once more I'll put some spirit of fire into him where the sun doesn't shine."

At last we got going at five to four. Although we weren't a full complement, Tripplehorn had secured the services of a couple of other singers including Charles Tyrebuck who'd been to France with us last summer, and had travelled specially down today from his home in Ripon. Matthew had given him the nickname Buck Tyrepump, much to his annoyance, after a somewhat surreal misunderstanding during a choir practice. His voice was no better this time. We'd rehearsed the piece enough times last night, but when after a couple of passable runthroughs this afternoon we decided to go for the real thing, our performance really was abysmal. However, following another four abortive attempts, we proceeded to deliver two really very acceptable versions and at last began to achieve some of the effect I'd been seeking when writing the piece during Lent. It was just a shame that for the first of those performances the engineer had forgotten to reset the Pause button, and that right at the end of the second a group of octogenarians wandered in and engaged in a very loud discussion as to whom they needed to consult before rubbing Sir Hector Duggleby's horsebrass.

Somehow we produced an uninterrupted recording that did not elicit a reaction from Tripplehorn which included some reference to basset hounds being fed through industrial mangles. Of course that may have been something to do with the fact that all the London contingent were now coming in, having rehearsed in the hall this afternoon, wishing to do a brief warm-up in the stalls before their evensong. I had hoped to attend the service but having decided that a decent and above all leisurely tea with Katie was now rather higher up my list of priorities, I made a speedy exit. I thought I saw Tripplehorn beckoning to me as I left, but after the frustrations of the afternoon I decided whatever it was he wanted could wait. As Katie and I relaxed over one of the Cosy Nook's delicious cream teas, I half wondered if he was going to suggest I might be interviewed by Doug Launchberry about my work. But after what had been said about him last night I had no wish to make further inroads into my free day explaining to him that polyphonic was a description of the style of page five of my piece. And not the name of the busty soprano two from the left on the second row.

Sunday 22nd June

Slept in so missed the broadcast of *Spirit Of Fire* completely. However a lot of people had heard it, and the vicar offered congratulations to us all during the service this morning, saying the choir had never performed so well. Better still, Anthony Cartwright produced the promised funds. The cheque was much bigger than expected and incredibly, despite all the setbacks, we are very nearly halfway to our target with over six months to go and the biggest events still to come.

Over coffee afterwards, I saw Tripplehorn standing alone so went over to him and thanked him for helping to make it all possible. "At one time yesterday afternoon I completely despaired of our ever doing a decent recording," I told him.

"So did I," said Tripplehorn, "which is why after you'd all gone I got the London choir to re-record it. I tried to call over to you to get you to stay so you could sing with them, or at least hear their version, but you seemed in rather a hurry to be away. In two takes they achieved a better result than we would have managed in a month of Sundays."

I nearly dropped my coffee cup. "Y-y-you mean to say that wasn't us on the radio this morning?" I spluttered.

"Of course not," he replied. "You don't think I'd allow that apology for a recording we did yesterday afternoon to go out on air, do you?"

"B-b-but what about Mr Bald Tyre? I mean, Mr Tyrebuck? He came all the way down from Ripon to get on the radio."

"Oh, he got on the radio all right," said Tripplehorn. "A little news tailpiece to the broadcast this morning about his unfortunate accident while the recording engineers were in the church."

"What accident?" I enquired.

"Oh, it happened as he was leaving," said Tripplehorn. "Apparently one of the engineers slipped on a loose paving stone and dropped a speaker on his foot."

Thursday 26th June

I never knew how difficult it could be to get genuine support from local traders for a local community effort. Until my day off today, that is.

Started promisingly enough, the charity shop in Queens Passage supplying an excellent cuddly pink giraffe free of charge, and, as the lady who served me pointed out, the lucky winner is unlikely to notice the egg yolk stain on its bottom. But of the twenty five shops I went into subsequently, only a handful were prepared to offer anything at all. Then again, since the vestry fund is not exactly the top priority good cause in our area I perhaps should count myself fortunate to have got what I did. The box of cut-price Cadbury's creme eggs from the discount supermarket on Friary Street will satisfy the cravings of even the most confirmed chocaholic, and the fact that the silver wrapping is now, some two months after the Easter festival for which the eggs were intended, virtually welded to the chocolate underneath simply adds to the anticipation of the feast. The set of assorted jams from Savemart certainly is beautifully packed; as long as there are pictures of the fruit on the labels, the fact that to read the list of ingredients and additives requires a Ukrainian interpreter really needn't deter potential bidders in the slightest. It was very nice of Sharon Jackson at the beauty parlour in the leisure centre complex to offer a leg waxing, even though the lucky winner will have to attend between 8.30am and 10.15am on a Monday in termtime and will have to pay to have the other leg done. The assistant manager of Bellis' Sports shop in Newmarket Lane said he'd be delighted to give a free tennis lesson; the prospective pupil will surely feel honoured to accept tuition from such a skilled exponent of the game, his prowess amply demonstrated by his having got through one of the preliminary regional Wimbledon pre-qualifying rounds in 1997, and we can only hope that his Achilles tendon which has kept him off court for the last eight months will clear up sometime this year. The meal for two at La Bonne Charcuterie is sure to be delicious, so much so that potential diners will certainly not mind that the voucher only covers two main courses and is conditional on a starter, sweet course, cheeseboard and coffee being ordered and paid for by the couple as well, and cannot be redeemed after 8pm, or at any time on Fridays, Saturdays, Valentine's Day or Mothering Sunday. And the hamper of goodies from the deli in Smith Street looks simply mouth-watering, so good in fact that the winner will have no difficulty getting through it all in the two days between the date of the auction and the Use By date stamped on the bottom of the box.

But all things being equal, it's a poor lookout when I count the biggest coup of the day to be Mrs Singh's no-strings-attached donation of three months' free service washes at the Wacky Wash-and-Go Parlour.

Friday 27th June

The dates for the Christmas play plus carols for choir and audience were announced to the choir tonight. The event will take place on Friday 5th and Saturday 6th December in the church hall. Auditions are confirmed as taking place next Sunday afternoon, with only present members of the choir being eligible to take part. I rather boldly asked Ruth what would happen if there were no suitable or indeed available members of the choir to take certain roles. "There will be," she said.

A more fundamental question was raised by Rachel. "I assume Frank's going to be MD'ing, but who's actually going to be producing the play?" she asked.

"Of course, I'd be the last person to want to stand in the way of anybody wanting to produce it," Ruth said with a frown, clearly astonished that anyone should think the question worth asking at all. "But if I were asked, I would of course be happy to volunteer my services in that regard."

So that was that then. Or so I thought. But as we proceeded with the practice, Craig Dumbleton leaned across to me and said "Actually, I would have been quite happy to produce."

Although he didn't broach the subject again during the practice, I was slightly concerned that Craig had not really had adequate opportunity to put his case to the members of the jury and might have legitimate grounds to attack the proceedings as breaching fundamental rules of natural justice. Over coffee afterwards, out of Craig's hearing, I approached Ruth and moved for interim relief pending a full rehearing.

Ruth deliberated for perhaps three and a half seconds, then delivered her judgement. "That's fine," she said, "if you're happy for a repetition of the last choir production he organised."

I asked when that was.

"Oh, you obviously weren't around that year," said Ruth. "When two people both arrived on opening night each thinking they were playing the lead, the health and safety officer shut the hall on the third night because of the pile of rubbish in the back corridor, the first of three acts didn't finish till quarter to ten, five of the twelve members of the chorus went on strike, the costumes didn't arrive until twenty minutes before curtain up on the first night and three people were without them anyway, and the dry ice machine he'd brought in specially blew one of the fuses and plunged the whole hall into darkness halfway through act two."

I don't think I'll bother to lodge an appeal.

Sunday 29th June

Six months more or less to the day that Katie and I became an item. She came to church with me this morning and, perhaps inspired by the Petertide sermon on the courage of commitment to Christ, has signed up to be confirmed by the Bishop in church in November.

Quite appropriate, somehow, that at this halfway point during my year's fundraising mission, I should have spent much of the evening occupied with Arthur's choir history script, which had been the first project presented to me at the start of the year. I had actually finished typing it a week or so ago and given it to him to check over, asking him to keep any alterations to an absolute minimum. Whether that actually made any difference to the final number of amendments I don't know, but an average of eight per page was certainly more than I had bargained for and a good deal in excess of what my blood pressure, particularly at nine forty five in the evening with a week's work to go to in barely ten hours' time, could reasonably be expected to stand.

I was however determined to get the final version emailed to Malcolm that night, so ploughed on, inspired by the sure and certain hope of spiritual reward for offering loving and uncomplaining service to our worship community. And by the fact that I'd promised myself two cut-price Cadbury's creme eggs when I finished. Finally at ten thirty with immense relief I pressed SAVE for the last time and was about to email it to Malcolm when the phone rang. It was Arthur.

"I don't quite know how to put this," Arthur said to me, "but I've forgotten the mango."

I told him that he must have the wrong number.

"No," he said. "I mean, I completely forgot to add into chapter 7 the wonderful story about the Victoria Passion we did in 1983 when we had to sing the words 'If thou let this man go' but because of the way the underlay was printed, it looked like 'If thou let this mango!!' So every time we did that piece subsequently we called it the mango piece! Don't you think that's absolutely hilarious!"

As I wearily scrolled back up to chapter 7, I half wondered whether to insert a health warning at the start of it. It would be a tragedy if any readers were to die of laughter and thus never get to read in chapter 8 of Gloria Farningdale's appointment as Acting Assistant Choir Librarian And Choir Outing Sandwich Cutter.

JULY

Friday 4th July

One of the first really hot days of the summer. Despite the fact that we've now started practising for the big evening concert and auction of promises on the 26th, Tripplehorn very considerately let us all out of tonight's practice a full twenty minutes early, telling us to "go off and have a swim, or something." Amazingly, I still don't think anyone's cottoned on that it wasn't us on the radio the other Sunday. Anthony Cartwright has provided a master tape of the broadcast and I overheard Cora saying she was going to send a copy to her cousin in Australia. I dare say the truth will come out soon enough, but there's no point in spoiling her fun. Who knows, it might be the last time anyone compliments Cora on her singing. Anyone, that is, except those who either want Cora's house for their next coffee morning, or whose eardrums are overdue for their 5000-mile servicing.

With ideas among the choir for possible promises for the auction apparently drying up, I had asked last Sunday for some more conventional prizes to be auctioned for and given away on the night. I felt I needed to be seen to be moving things forward, especially as Ruth had asked me to join her for a planning meeting on Tuesday week in order that we could discuss progress. Maybe I was pushing my luck tonight, with swimming pools as well as long cool glasses of Pimms beckoning, but I wasn't hugely encouraged by tonight's response. Alison Sparkes' late mother's digital alarm clock, which apparently has a strange aversion to moving off 4.37 and 28 seconds would, I presumed, be susceptible to some form of surgery. Matthew Sparkes' *Even More Annoying Joke Book* was probably past redemption of any kind. And the less said about Henry Peasgood's brother-in-law's collection of 1987 pocket timetables of the Zurich suburban tramway system the better.

Sunday 6th July

A lovely service this morning although we were rather depleted on the soprano line. I somehow doubt that the need to prepare for this afternoon's auditions was the reason for it. Indeed, Ruth said to me "In my experience, the better prepared someone is for an audition, the more incompetent it's likely to be."

The auditions began at 2.15pm in the church hall before an auditioning committee consisting of Ruth Hartnell, Ruth Hartnell and Ruth Hartnell, in no particular order. No problem with the first audition, for the mischievous boy soprano Billy; even though it was a foregone conclusion Matthew would get it, I was impressed with his ingenuity in bringing along a yo-yo and a giant bargain pack of Savemart fruit gums as props.

He worked them brilliantly into his audition. Ken did a superb job as Jolyon Winklethorpe, the blundering and incompetent vicar, and I felt pleased enough with my portrayal of Edward Harper, who provides one half of the love interest in the play. The only competition among the male parts was between Arthur Ramsbottom and Henry Peasgood who both put in for Vic Crabtree, the only bass in the fictional choir of the play and well known for being an interfering busybody. Arthur's performance was really quite pitiful, and although Henry's was hardly in the Laurence Olivier class, none of us were left in any doubt as to who was the stronger candidate.

With half the auditions done, and ten minutes to spare before we were due to start the auditions for the female parts, Ruth announced that the audition committee had all agreed to adjourn for a tea break in the kitchen adjoining the main hall, and to my surprise I found myself summoned into the kitchen to meet the members. "Just wanted to confirm with you the male parts," she said. "Matthew, Ken, yourself and Arthur."

"Arthur?" I echoed.

"Of course," said Ruth. "I've certainly no intention of having Henry Peasgood getting on my nerves for the next five months. The man's a born pain in the backside. The only reason Frank puts up with him in the choir is because he's able to get hold of sets of music for him on the cheap."

"I hope he doesn't throw a strop when you tell him he's not got the part," I said with a rather nervous giggle.

"Oh, that's taken care of," said Ruth airily. "When I produced the Christmas panto in my previous parish, I developed a very straightforward procedure for dealing with anyone who challenges audition decisions. It's virtually foolproof. I'd tell them I had an extremely important role for them in the production, either front of house or backstage, that was tailor-made to suit their particular talents and aptitudes."

"And what if there was no such role?" I queried.

"I told them that St Tropez is very nice in the winter months," Ruth replied.

And so, on to the auditions for the female parts. We first dealt easily with the audition for Eugenia Raggett, the ageing prima donna of the fictional choir; Cora was of course hopeless but such is her influence that Ruth had no choice but to give her whatever she wanted even if it meant excusing her from all but the dress rehearsal and allocating her a private dressing room with interval sherries and masseuse. There was some good-natured rivalry between Rachel and Alison for the part of Shirley Dewhurst, a somewhat scatterbrained choir member with a propensity for dropping books and pieces of music at the most inconvenient moment, and there

96

was very little to choose between them. However Alison's limited availability, owing apparently to Zoe's promotion in her Brownie pack to Brown Owl's Big Helper and Chief Blackcurrant Juice Monitor, effectively removed any uncertainty as to which of them would secure the role. I expected no competition for the part of the choirmistress, Sylvia Wheelwright, although anyone who had the temerity to put themselves up against each and every member of the audition committee and expect to have a chance of getting the part must have more misplaced bravado than an Atlantic sailor putting out to sea equipped with nothing more than a bathtub, golfing umbrella and a bar of Cadbury's Fruit & Nut. To our collective astonishment, Joan Trumpington decided to put in for the part, but as Ruth so diplomatically put it, "I can quite sympathise with anyone forgetting their first line, jumping three speeches, transposing all the words of a six-line speech, and then delivering a line intended for somebody else. It's a bit harder to understand when they've got the script in front of them while they're doing it."

That left the part of Claudette, a new and dazzlingly attractive choir member from France, and the other half of the love interest. Margaret Pardew, bless her, tried for the part, but it was no surprise when the audition committee announced a unanimous verdict that the role in question could not yet be cast. In a way I felt quite sorry for the hapless applicant. But as Ruth put it, one has to be cruel to be kind, and where box office takings are of such vital importance, there can be no place as a romantic lead for someone as convincing in her Gallic guile and charm as the chief village idiot of Llanvihangel Crucorney.

Friday 11th July

Having phoned Ruth last night to ask whom she had in mind for the part of Claudette, she would only say that it would all be settled immediately after tonight's practice. The whole business had rather gone out of my head as we worked somewhat laboriously through the first half of the programme for the 26th following a quick canter through the music that we were doing on Sunday. It was thus to my amazement that the door opened, just as we were coming to the end of the practice, to admit Jane Markwick, followed shortly afterwards by a slightly built elderly man with whitish hair and bushy eyebrows. She'd often spoken to me about her grandfather, Lesley's dad, but I'd never actually seen him. Impulsively, and hardly waiting for Tripplehorn to announce that he was calling it a night, I raced down the aisle to greet her and was rewarded with a big hug and a kiss on both cheeks. It really was brilliant to see her again after so many months. Despite the age disparity between us, I had had quite a crush on her for much of last year and had she not got herself engaged to a liberally tattooed mushroom grower from Leighton Buzzard

97

last Christmas, I might never have got together with Katie. The irony being that apparently the mushroom grower has now gone off backpacking in Namibia with a hotel chambermaid from Steeple Bumpstead.

I love Katie to bits but I would be lying if I said my heart didn't give a leap at the sight of Jane, her short skirt showing off her astonishingly long slim legs, and her medium height elevated by her huge high-heeled sandals. Although I have now been with Katie for six months, and I'm sure Jane must have had an army of admirers of her own in that time, there's a part of me that has never quite gone off her. I was accordingly thrilled to have it confirmed that she has indeed been asked by Ruth to audition for the part of Claudette. "I know it's supposed to be for existing choir members only," Jane said with a smile that would have melted a deep-frozen Fox's Glacier Mint, "but I don't think I ever did tender my resignation, did I?" It was all I could do not to seize her in my arms, drag her to the north transept beneath the memorial effigies, and make mad passionate love to her there and then under the disapproving eye of Lady Eleanor Fortinbrace.

Putting such carnal thoughts to the back of my mind, I did ask Jane if she – Jane, that is, not Lady Eleanor Fortinbrace – would like to join me for a drink. To my disappointment she couldn't, as she was meeting a couple of friends in town, but there was enough time after what was a formality of an audition for her to be able to fill me in on her university course and her summer holiday plans. She'd passed her first year exams with flying colours and was to be spending three weeks of her vacation in New Zealand before returning to uni for the autumn term. I asked her how she was going to find time to get to all the rehearsals for the play. "Oh, Ruth told me just to come when I can," she said. "She says that as long as I turn up on the night with a functioning set of limbs and knowing more than half of my lines I'll be better prepared than two thirds of the rest of the cast."

That I can well believe.

The precious minutes we had seemed to pass all too quickly. When the time came for her to go, she gave me a whopping kiss and told me she couldn't wait to work with me on the play, promising that she'll take me for a drink after the first rehearsal for which she is available, so we can enjoy a really good long chat. I'm ashamed to say that despite my relationship with Katie, I felt really quite excited at the prospect. Jane was somehow different from how I'd remembered her, but in a nice way: she was still as exuberant and bubbly as ever, but she seemed to have shed the rather irritating girlishness that had made a fool out of me once too often last year, and had led to her making so many unwise choices in terms of her personal relationships. It did appear that all that was in the past and she was now becoming a remarkably attractive and desirable young woman with the whole world at her feet.

As I walked her to the door, I pointed to the diminutive old man who was wandering down the aisle with Lesley towards us. "Nice to meet your grandad at last," I told her.

"Grandad?" she echoed. "He's my boyfriend. I moved in with him last month."

Sunday 13th July

I'm not sure whether I was pleased or disappointed that Jane was not around for church this morning. I could hardly bring myself to look at Lesley, still less speak to her. Tripplehorn told me off afterwards for singing the anthem with so little conviction. But since the anthem in question was Hadley's *My Beloved Spake*, I could have been forgiven for treating it, in his words, as though I was reciting the contents of a local government directive on the correct positioning of household wheelie bins.

The general gloom increased afterwards when Ruth said she wanted to get in at least two rehearsals for the play before the end of the month. "I'm away virtually throughout August," she said, "but if we can have one evening's readthrough and one evening's plotting of the moves, that'll have laid the ground for when the really serious work starts in September."

We found that, Jane excepted obviously, we were all available for a plotting rehearsal on the night of Wednesday 30th, which is the day before Ruth flies out to her holiday retreat in Tuscany. The problem was finding a suitable date for the readthrough meeting when all of us were free. Cora was, perhaps predictably, the main stumbling block, with all her committees, subcommittees and steering groups. She has fingers in so many pies I'm surprised she's not changed her name by deed poll to Little Jack Horner. In the end it came down to a choice between next Sunday afternoon, which I was really hoping to avoid because I had promised to go for lunch and tea with Katie's parents as a belated treat for my birthday the day before, and early evening the following day, which was marginally more convenient for me although would still mean my having to eat into my flexitime at work. It was Ruth who then announced that owing to a commitment at the local magistrates' court on the Monday afternoon, that was out and we would therefore be rehearsing on the Sunday. She said to me tersely "There are lots of other Sundays in the year when you can go lunching with relations."

I could almost feel the steam coming out of my ears as I left. Rachel, who walked with me down the path, seemed to sense my fury and did her best to cheer me up. "Her mentioning the magistrates' court reminds me of a hilarious incident in court I heard of about a month ago," she said. "They were dealing with some twopenny-halfpenny case, unlicensed poaching or some such drivel. Anyway a witness comes into the court room and this pompous old battleaxe of a magistrate on the bench says 'You must answer audibly to every question.' So the witness is asked 'Where were you on the night of the 16th January?' And he replies 'Audibly!'"

"Yes, I remember it well," said Ruth as she came up from behind. "I was the magistrate."

I somehow think that's both of us in the detention book already. Before rehearsals have even started.

Tuesday 15th July

A planning meeting at Ruth's house tonight for Saturday week. Craig Dumbleton was there too, having offered to help with some of the practical arrangements on the night. Very much as expected, Ruth Hartnell did virtually all of the talking. She spent some time telling us about the performers, or artistes as she insisted on calling them, and gave us brief summaries of their careers to date. There are half a dozen artistes in all, each in their twenties, and although they are not household names yet, nor do their claims to fame make particularly impressive reading, she was at pains to point out that events such as these would do them no harm whatsoever in raising their profile, particularly as she had persuaded most of the bigwigs in the local community to come along on the night. She also hinted that she had invited "some quite influential people in the music world." Whoever they may be.

"Ticket sales are going extremely well," she went on. "I expect to double the amount the vestry fund has raised so far simply on the basis of this function alone."

I was tempted to suggest that if she thought my efforts hitherto had been so inept she should simply take over all the vestry fundraising from now on, but before I could say anything she'd moved rapidly on to the finer details of the evening, from the welcoming committee for the artistes through to those responsible for leaving the empty wine bottles out for recycling when the function finished at midnight.

"And of course," she said, "We need to consider the personal requests of the artistes. Three of them have asked for a vegetarian meal, which is no problem at all. The bassoonist has asked for a certain type of mineral water which I believe you can only get from Fortnums in London so I shall be in touch with them to arrange that. The harpist would like a quiet room for ten minutes or so before going on in order to meditate, the trumpeter is allergic to cats, and the counter-tenor wishes to gargle with raw egg."

I dutifully noted down the requirements and accepted those I was individually required to see to. All the same, I can't help feeling that it's asking quite a lot of me to oversee the removal of Cora's notoriously aggressive Siamese from the proceedings. I certainly do not wish to risk compromising the highest possible standards of performance, but I see no need to go to such extreme lengths, especially as none of these artistes can really claim to have achieved celebrity status. Take the harpist for instance. Whose sole claim to fame seems to consist of having premiered a piece by a Czech composer nobody had ever heard of at a concert almost attended by the acting deputy Czech cultural attaché.

Friday 18th July
An excellent start to the day, Martin Perry ringing me at breakfast to say he will agree, as part of the auction of promises, to cloth-bind a paperback book of the highest bidder's choice. He added that as his daughter was shortly flying out to New Zealand to set up her permanent home there, he was sure she wouldn't miss some of her childhood toys and he'd throw in her fluffy purple rhinoceros as well.

Ruth phoned a little later. Fortunately, she confirmed that she thinks we now have about the right number of promises and prizes. The reason for her ringing was to tell me that she has had to go away for a couple of days and to ask if I would I speak to the local press about next Saturday so we can get a spread in next week's paper and perhaps achieve a sellout. I wasn't ecstatic about doing so. For one thing, I had a lot of work on my desk, and for another, the local paper is not exactly the most riveting read of the week.

I asked Ruth if there was any particular reason why she thought I would be better suited to the task than her.

"I wanted to speak to Colin Diamond but he doesn't start his shift till midday, and by then I'll be gone," she said.

I enquired why it was necessary to speak to Colin Diamond in particular as there are a number of arts reporters on the staff of the paper.

"He does have one special characteristic that makes him unique among its reporters," she explained.

I asked her what that was.

"A brain," she replied.

Before she left, she emailed me details not only of the artistes but some of the local dignitaries who were supporting the event as well. I had intended to use this merely as the basis for my interview with Mr Diamond. But when I finally got through to him at twenty past four the novelty of ringing his office to be told "He's just popped out he shouldn't be long" had worn off to such an extent that I found myself doing little more than reading almost verbatim the material Ruth had emailed me in the hope that he could make it into a moderately readable piece. I suspect however that even if he managed to combine the perceptive reportage of Samuel Pepys, the unashamed candour of Bernard Levin, the dazzling wit of Oscar Wilde and the frontline robustness of Kate Adie, he would have difficulty in persuading those otherwise tempted by barbecues, pool parties and Test matches to rub shoulders with those have done nothing more glamorous to earn their OBE's and MBE's than a lifetime's work as morning receptionist in the town's veterinary surgery or fourteen years' once-weekly strimming of the hedges round the social security benefit office.

Tonight at choir we spent some time discussing future fundraising events after the big one tomorrow week. Apart from the play and concert in December, the diary is blank. Motivation to think of some new ideas was not enhanced by the hot muggy weather, and the whinges amongst the membership tonight over the cost of the tickets for next Saturday. It did not help matters that Ruth Hartnell was away. The truth is that they'd never have dared try it on with her. One glance from her is usually enough to convince most right-thinking people that there would be less risk to one's future prospects in smuggling a thousand holdalls full of crack cocaine out of Chile. Or trying to pay by cheque for nine items in the eight items or less queue in Savemart on a Saturday morning.

Sunday 20th July

Katie rang me first thing to check what time we were setting off to her parents for lunch, and I realised I'd quite forgotten to tell her I was unable to make it because of this wretched afternoon rehearsal. She was absolutely furious, her harsh words putting me in quite the wrong frame of mind for church. We were singing one of my favourite works, Wesley's *Blessed Be The God And Father*, but I was quite unable to enjoy a single syllable of it.

Early cloud and drizzle soon disappeared and it turned into a glorious sunny afternoon with temperatures climbing into the high twenties. It seemed all the more ridiculous to be spending the afternoon indoors at Ruth's house rehearsing for a play about Christmas carol-singing. Apart from Jane, we were all there: Matthew, Arthur, Cora, Ken, Rachel, Ruth and myself. From the readthrough it soon became clear which sections would work best and which were going to pose real challenges to Ruth as producer. The scenes, for instance, involving Ruth and Ken together were most enjoyable and if they were asked to perform them tomorrow they would probably be able to do so. By contrast, the short section featuring Arthur and Matthew together prompted mental pictures of the earliest days of the most rudimentary dental extraction. The most unedifying part of the afternoon consisted of Cora reading in for Jane, especially when we reached a whole page of dialogue between Cora's character Eugenia and Jane's character Claudette. Paradoxically, the spectacle might actually have been moderately entertaining, had it not been for the fact that Cora's impression of a young ravishing female was the least convincing since King Ethelburg the Hirsute put on a wig of shredded paper and attempted to gatecrash his way into the AD985 Miss South East Denmark competition.

As I was leaving, too late to even contemplate driving up to Katie's parents, but too early for *The Best Of Pets Do The Funniest Things*, Ruth tackled me about Saturday. She told me she needed to check over the list of prizes and promises, and agree a minimum price for each. Apparently she wants to prepare a proper schedule and proformas so that as people arrive they can put in bids in advance, thereby saving a great deal of time during the auction itself. Fortunately I had the list of prizes and promises with me, and proudly produced it, thinking as I did so how kind the local townsfolk had been and how reassuring it was to know we had so much support for the project.

She ran her eye down the list, then drew in her breath sharply and raised her eyebrows a few hundred notches. "My dear boy, they must have seen you coming," she said. "I could do better than that with my eyes shut."

And from having fondly believed that I had completed the task, I now, even with Ruth's promised assistance, have the best part of a week's work ahead of me in endeavouring to persuade the benefactors to be a little more open-handed with their generosity. The charity shop that provided the pink cuddly toy apparently has two big boxes full of children's toys which will never be offered for sale but are simply given away to kids whose mothers make purchases exceeding fifty pence. Bearing in mind that Hair Is The News is singularly devoid of customers at just about any time of day, there is no apparent reason why the free cut and blow-dry needs to be administered at 7.30am on a Tuesday. And the voucher issued by In Vision entitling the bearer to fifty per cent off the purchase of a video cassette would be rather more welcome, Ruth maintained, if the shop owner were to agree to reconsider his decision to withdraw all video cassettes in favour of DVD's two days after the auction.

By the time we agreed our strategy, my long-anticipated television treat had gone the same way as my lunch with Katie and her family. Ah well. I dare say the aniseed ball juggling dog will be repeated on the Christmas special edition.

Friday 25th July

Excellent news at lunchtime, as over the phone Ruth and I agreed the final definitive list of prizes and promises, together with the minimum prices for all of them. All I've got to worry about now on the night is dealing with that wretched cat.

Following a lengthy practice for all our pieces for tomorrow night, we then had to sit through a very lengthy briefing meeting. Henry Peasgood and Arthur Ramsbottom, who'd both been away all week, were the only absentees. Ruth explained that she'd engaged a firm of top caterers from London to prepare the food; they will bring all the ingredients with them and use Cora's more than ample facilities. "They're a curious outfit," she said. "They're actually Italians with fairly limited command of English and they're very unassuming, even down to their choice of transport – they go round in this rusty old white van. But the quality of the food is absolutely sky-high."

And their prices, if the copy correspondence she produced to us was anything to go by.

Ruth also told us she had some "really exciting news." A contact of hers is features editor of a new magazine called *Fifty And Proud Of It*. Ruth didn't have a copy but apparently it is designed for the "discerning and wannabe-upwardly-mobile but sassy and sophisticated fifty-something" and the editor has decided to cover tomorrow's event for a forthcoming issue. The camera crew will be arriving around three fifteen to start setting up and will then be taking pictures of the house and grounds before the party begins.

"I can't say I've heard of this super-duper magazine," Alison said with a giggle.

"Well, you have now," Ruth snapped with the speed and precision of a marauding piranha. "It obviously has a fair way to go to compete with the major glossies and it's up to us by the quality of the food, company and surroundings to give them the best possible spread to assist them to increase their market share."

So be it. But I somehow can't see the editors of *Hello!* and *OK!* shaking in their boots at the thought of a would-be rival publication whose most provocative and daring photographic scoop of the week consisted of Eileen Crosby remonstrating with the County Council chief executive about his waste recycling initiatives through a mouthful of stuffed olive.

Saturday 26th July

The day of the party had come at last, and with Katie having to work, I had offered to be at Cora's to assist with the final arrangements from three onwards. Before I left, I rang Malcolm to ask for an update on the progress of the choir history. He told me he was rather tied up but would get back to me sometime today. I was saddened, but not surprised, that my mobile remained silent for the rest of the afternoon and evening.

Having agreed with Ruth that I would welcome the camera crew and give them any assistance they might need, I was delighted when they duly appeared two minutes early. Ruth was already there, brimful of energy, and speaking confidently of a spectacular success in the making. Her joie de vivre was, however, temporarily halted when Arthur Ramsbottom appeared, clutching his camcorder and speaking into the microphone in a hushed conspiratorial voice. He had a slightly older man with him, apparently equally absorbed with the filming process.

"Will you please tell me what you're doing?" Ruth demanded. She sounded like a teacher scolding a couple of errant schoolboys. "Are you not aware that *Fifty And Proud Of It* have exclusive rights to film this event?"

To give him his due, Arthur stood his ground. "I'm not proposing to sell my film," he said. "It is just for the choir archive. My friend Stan's giving me a hand."

But his brave words were dismissed with all the respect the Brazilian national football team might have for a Sunday park side they were already beating 15-0 at half time. "I don't think so," said Ruth. "Now will you please switch that thing off and could you get out unless there's something you feel you can help with. And take your friend with you please. There's enough going on here without the place being knee-deep in unwanted intruders."

For one mad, crazy moment I thought Arthur was going to argue, but Stan had already taken his leave with the vigour of a startled gazelle, and, giving up the unequal struggle, the self-appointed archivist slunk away upstage left.

When they had gone, Ruth turned her attention to the official camera crew. However if she felt she could impose her iron will upon the photographers she was in for a rude awakening. Although two of the three were very down to earth and quite happy to take pictures of anything or anyone within reach, the principal member of the trio was as demanding as Catherine The Great on a bad hair day. By the time he had made a list of the various moves required for the music room furniture, and the complex adjustments to the coloured lighting over the piano stool, we were running twenty minutes behind schedule and there was no sign of the caterers who should have arrived half an hour before. Ruth, who'd planned to meet them at the end of her drive but admitted that in attending to the demands of the camera crew she had forgotten about them, was now seriously concerned that they might have missed the turning and got lost.

As we were debating what to do next, Henry Peasgood arrived with two young men whom he introduced to me as his nephews and who were acting as wine waiters for the evening. "Sorry we're a bit late," he said. "Bit of road rage down at the end of your drive."

"Eh?" Ruth retorted suspiciously. "What do you mean?"

"Oh," said Henry, "Arthur and his friend flagged down this filthy white van full of foreign-looking types. Sent them packing. Told them he'd been instructed not to allow any more unwanted intruders into the place. They got a bit shirty and one of them started some cock and bull story about providing food for tonight. Nobody was falling for that. I think you should thank Arthur. He's done you a favour."

If only the cameras had been able to record the look on Ruth's face.

Unfortunately but perhaps predictably, the chastened caterers did not seem in the slightest bit of a hurry to answer either their office phone or their mobile phone. Meanwhile, I was advised that there was some "news" about the instrumentalist with the cat allergy. I hoped either that he had found some suitable remedy or, better still, that he wasn't coming at all, but sadly it was neither. The message was now that he had an allergy to cat fur as well as the live article, and that he was arriving in an hour. As a result, I was entrusted with the responsibility of detecting and removing every single feline hair from the reception areas of Cora's sizeable dwelling. Since the hot weather had resulted in the animal shedding sizeable chunks of its winter coat on to virtually every item of furniture, as well as into the fabric of her carpets, it was a task that even the most vicious Soviet labour camp guard would have thought twice about inflicting upon his mother-in-law. The job was done with five minutes to spare, meaning that I had just five minutes to catch the cat, who was skulking angrily in the kitchen, and deposit it in the box room upstairs. Despite Cora's promise that "he'll be fine, I assure you," it was twenty minutes later that I found myself hurrying to greet the musician with a tightly bandaged hand, while Cora herself hastened to remove from harm's way a waste-paper bin now full of tissue containing what was surely sufficient blood to satisfy the demands of every donor clinic within a radius of a hundred miles.

As I did so, Ruth was reporting back with exceedingly gloomy news about the caterers. "I managed to track them down halfway up the M4," she said. "They'll be with us by seven."

We all gasped. That was three hours behind schedule. We held an urgent conference and decided that the best plan was to cancel the original arrangement and instead of having the meal first followed by the entertainment and then the auction, we would organise the canapés ourselves, prolong the drinks and nibbles as long as we could, then intersperse the entertainment with the food as and when it became ready.

Meanwhile, Arthur Ramsbottom was looking at career opportunities in the foothills of the Himalayas.

I will say this for the unlikely team of chefs in their rust-coated white van. After the initial protestations and their understandable observation "If you think we cook this meal which take-a the three hours in a twenty minutes, you have the other think coming," they knuckled down with commendable zeal, doubtless spurred on by a desire to impress the assembled company with their traditional native industry, and enhance their credibility as a flexible and well managed organisation. The £20 notes Ruth slipped to each of them may have served as a small additional motivating factor. Fearful that as time slipped by, we might start to lose some of the guests, we decided to do the auction following the first set of choir items and some instrumental pieces. Thankfully our singing went well, but our work was followed by a somewhat inept performance from the harpist who was the first alleged celebrity to go on. It was of course not his fault but that of Henry Peasgood, who had denied him the final two and a half minutes of his meditation by dropping a plateful of Savemart de luxe anchovies on to the wooden floor of the conservatory. We moved hastily on to the auction, which thanks to the work Ruth had done in advance did proceed steadily and also very lucratively after a slow start. It was disappointing that nobody seemed to have sufficient confidence in Henry Peasgood's niece's computer skills to take up her offer to type any handwritten piece of up to 10,000 words providing the handwriting was in black ink, on one side of paper only and legible throughout, and everybody was evidently too health conscious to feel able to bid for four months' free supply of bread rolls from Mr Bunright the baker's in Queen's Parade. Perhaps it was these early setbacks which pricked the consciences of some of the guests into making bids for items or services which seemed somewhat unsuited to them. I am a little apprehensive as to whether the sunlounger kindly donated by Ken Foulkes' daughter and son-in-law will bear the nineteen and a half stone of Roger Renton Arbuthnot, vice president of the local Rotary Club and reputedly founder member of Pork Pie Gorgers Anonymous. And although a week in Rachel Ellis' hairdresser's holiday apartment on the Costa del Sol is undoubtedly highly therapeutic to the beneficiary, I don't think I was alone in wondering whether Howard Gladestry, now in his late eighties and with more metal replacements in his body than a second-hand Ford Capri, would actually make it to the airport in the first place.

Unfortunately, the clock was ticking away, stomachs were rumbling, and it was with relief rather than happy anticipation of a delicious meal that the assembly of guests sat down for the first course at twenty past nine. With a further delay before the main course, we got through all the remaining choir items and all but the grand finale of the instrumental work, which we had decided to save to the very end of the evening. That, however, was before we knew that the dessert would not be placed on the table till a quarter to midnight, and by eleven fifteen, with the main course just finished, we had lost the acting County Solicitor and the deputy chairman of the local bench of magistrates. At that stage the trumpeter had not played a single note, his role restricted to the grand finale, but sadly his allergy to cats was coupled with a decidedly diffident nature and his requests to be placed in the pecking order before the milk train set off from the up platform and the town's taxi drivers changed to quadruple time mode simply were not heard. Meanwhile the evening's overheads were rising exponentially. Ruth was now stuck with having to pay the musicians additional rates for staying on beyond ten thirty, as well as having to offer the guests free wine above the single glass per head to which they had been rationed, and every minute the guests remained, the more alcohol was being consumed, reducing still further the credit Fine Wines in Finkle Street would give us on any unused supplies. From having the potential to be one of the most financially successful events of the year, it now looked unlikely to make us any money at all.

It was not until twenty minutes past midnight, with guests filtering away into the night including the Lord Lieutenant, last year's Mayoress, the vice chairman of the town's netball team and the owner of the town's mobile discotheque, that Ruth announced the grand trumpet finale. Just before the trumpeter proceeded to the rostrum, however, a singularly merry Dr Carter, the town's leading chiropodist, rolled up to me and asked me where the "Lent's Jew" was.

I was tempted to tell him "Upstairs, first roar on the dight," but not knowing when I might need professional assistance to burst the blister on my right heel, I bit it back – the comment, not the blister – and watched him lurch off in the direction of the guest bathroom. It was only when he was two thirds of the way up that I decided it might be as well to go after him and ensure that he did not enter the adjacent box room by mistake. But I was too late, for seconds later he threw open the box room door and out bounded Cora's sabre-toothed Siamese. In the space of thirty seconds the pent-up frustration of several hours' imprisonment exploded into an unprovoked scratching attack on the town's assistant sub-postmistress, the destruction of six priceless Royal Doulton dinner plates, and the precipitous despatch of a sneezing wheezing trumpeter out of the French windows and straight into Cora's ornamental fishpond.

Since the grand trumpet finale was now missing a grand trumpeter, the remaining guests wasted little time in departing, together with the camera team.

"I suppose at least you've got some good copy for your magazine," I told one of them as they proceeded out of the front door. "When will we see it in print?"

"I doubt you will, to be honest," he said. "It's only a fairly new outfit and we're having problems in paying our distributors so chances are it won't find its way down this neck of the woods at all. We've plenty round our way though and there's one store that always carries it."

"You mean one of the big stores? Asda or Tesco?" I asked with rising hope.

"Not quite," he said, pausing to manoeuvre his equipment through the door. "It's Mags N Fags, Upper Colebrook Street, Newport Pagnell."

Sunday 27th July

Tripplehorn's last Sunday with us until late August. "I've managed to get Mike Pitheavlis to do the Sunday after next," he said, "but as for the others, don't be surprised if you get hymns stuck in the middle of the Eucharistic Prayer. Or a recessional hymn that's so long that you're singing six verses in the vestry. And when it's Pie Face Petherbridge, try and stop him snoring during the sermon. It'll only wake the rest of the congregation up."

Still tired after last night's debacle, I returned from church in a foul mood, and took my frustrations out on Malcolm's mobile telephone voicemail service. Astonishingly, as I was halfway through telling him that he had the communication skills of an asthmatic hedgehog and asking him what part of "IQ of minus 20" he did not understand, I heard his voice on the other end. I felt strangely and unaccountably guilty suddenly, and all the guiltier when he poured out the tale of woe that had befallen him over the past four weeks, from the broken fan belt he'd sustained just past Junction 18 on the M1 in the evening rush hour to ruining his best suit by slipping on a puddle of orange juice in Pret A Manger in Euston Road. All of these things, he said, had put him well behind with all the projects he was managing at the present time, but he assured me that the final material for printing and binding would be ready next Sunday for me to check over, including the illustrations.

However, not for nothing had I listened to Katie's words of wisdom on how to be assertive. I told him I insisted on his providing me with his home address, a landline telephone number, and an undertaking that if the material had not been emailed to me by five next Sunday afternoon I would consider the whole contract cancelled.

"You've been watching too much of Esther Robinson's *Watchdog*, haven't you?" he said.

Clearly he hasn't.

Katie telephoned me tonight offering to treat me to a pub meal at the Drovers, a beautiful country inn fifteen minutes' drive away, on Wednesday night, which is the one evening this week when we're both free. She tells me that locally produced ham and eggs is their speciality, and the sticky toffee pudding with custard is apparently in with a chance of winning National Pub Pud Of The Year competition.

The prospect of sitting in the pub garden over this delicious food and fine wine on a balmy summer's evening, watching the sun set over Collingbury Down, was irresistible.

Or would have been, had I not realised five minutes after accepting her invitation that that night we had our first plotting rehearsal for *See Amid*.

"Oh well," said Katie irritably, as I rang to break the joyous news that I could not go out with her on Wednesday evening after all. "Whatever you think is more important to you, I suppose." I felt smaller than a directory of Dorothy Perkins branches in Tanganyika.

Wednesday 30th July

Well, to her credit, Ruth did not hang around; she simply wanted to talk us through our moves, and act out only the sections of dialogue around entrances and exits. Once again, Cora took it upon herself to read in for Claudette, and it was to my intense annoyance that for some reason Ruth decided to get me to act through my love scene with her. In the circumstances, I think I could have been forgiven for going through the motions with as much conviction as the chairman of a football team at the foot of the table announcing a vote by the directors of absolute confidence in the manager. At that precise moment, I really did think that if Jane were not doing the part, and say Margaret Pardew had got it instead, I would distance myself from my part in the play altogether. Even if that meant taking up temporary residence in The Very Remote Cottage, Extremely Long Bumpy And Winding Road End, Outermost Patagonia.

At the end of the evening, Ruth said to me "I've got some excellent news. After a huge amount of phoning round, I've got an understudy for you to rehearse with you in Jane's absence. She's very keen and highly motivated, and says she can't wait to get working on the floor with you. I think you'll be pleased."

I could barely refrain from licking my lips in anticipation. Who might this be, I wondered. Lord Buttermere's youngest daughter, a stunning drama graduate in her early twenties? Or perhaps someone from the world of films. Kate Winslet? Julia Roberts? Or even my idol during my early thirties, Meg Ryan? "Go on, then," I said, "who is she?"

"Margaret Pardew," said Ruth.

AUGUST

Sunday 3rd August

The first of four Sundays without Tripplehorn. We had a guest organist, Donald Dewberry, who'd been away all last week so hadn't been able to practise with us on Friday. Although it had been undeniably nice to have the Friday night off, and thus enjoy a meal with Katie in the Drovers after all, it meant we were rather ill-prepared for our musical contribution this morning. The music was hardly demanding but the Margaret Rizza anthem we were doing had so many Da Capo and repeat markings in it, some printed and some pencilled in, that it wasn't surprising to see two of the basses working their way down page 34 while Arthur was still limping across the top line of page 32 and Craig was cruising along the bottom of page 38.

Returned from my afternoon out with Katie and saw a package stuffed into my letter box. I ripped it open to discover a bundle of paper and a scrawled note attached to the front of it which read "Herwith camera-ready copy to go to printer's for your finale approval, also invoice, cover pic and blyrb." The cover picture, consisting of group photos of the choir in 1930 and three years ago, had been scanned quite well and looked really very professional. But then I turned to the blurb, or even blyrb, the very first line of which turned "St Basil's started with a choir of six" to "St Basil's started with a choir of sex." Which set the scene for what followed.

And so to the body of the text. I had assumed that Malcolm would have had no difficulty in generating the camera-ready copy from the emailed material I had sent him, but I had obviously assumed wrong. I saw straight away that two paragraphs in the first two pages stopped in the middle of nowhere; the third page of text bore the page number eight and the fifth page bizarrely boasted the number one hundred and thirty six; and the last two pages of chapter two consisted of an unintelligible mass of symbols and numbers that could have been the vital missing page from Fermat's Last Theorem or the latest submission of local surrealist designer Aloysius Oppodopolous to the World of Wacky Modern Art Exhibition in the Shire Hall, Much Dewchurch.

Malcolm had at least provided an address to which I was to send my cheque in settlement, and although it was a good hour's drive away I decided to go straight round to confront him with his abysmal work in person. His property turned out to be a sizeable semi-detached house, with a very smart car parked in the driveway, and certainly didn't look the sort of place one would expect to see targeted by Esther Robinson. There was no electric fencing round the perimeter, nor any sign warning that unwelcome visitors would be eaten, and although I heard the noise of a dog barking it sounded less like a savage Alsatian than an irate Pekingese whose Pedigree Chum had been insufficiently liberally coated with Winalot. I rang the bell and stood waiting for five minutes, but there was no response. Even the disgruntled Peke seemed to give up his vocal exercises during my vigil.

I then became aware of a young man and woman appearing from round the side of the neighbouring property, so I told them I was looking for a man called Malcolm.

"Oh," said the man, "You mean the one wanted by the Inland Revenue for forging six years' worth of self-assessments, by the County Court for failing to deliver up bank documents with a view to enforcement of an order freezing his assets, and by the Crown Court for failing to appear on charges of fraudulent trading, embezzlement and obtaining a pecuniary advantage by deception. That Malcolm."

Feeling somewhat numb inside, I told them I suspected that was exactly who I was looking for.

"Shame," the man said. "You just missed him. He's just been chauffeured off for a free meal. Or rather, about five years' worth of free meals."

Friday 8th August

It seems miracles do happen after all. Having told the vicar the whole sorry story of Malcolm's novel interpretation of straight business dealing, I got a call today from Roger Endacott, the manager of a comparatively newly-established firm of printers in a neighbouring town. He has said that if I email the text to him, he will look at it and endeavour to print from it at an even more reasonable cost than Malcolm had quoted.

A very brief rehearsal tonight to go through Sunday's music with Mike Pitheavlis. It was a rather more ambitious selection than last Sunday's, hence the need for a practice, but since Mike's idea of rehearsal is to go through it once and if at least two people have reached the final page at the same time as him he pronounces himself happy with it, we were done by eight. I was thus in a position to get home in time to take a call from Roger Endacott who told me he has received my text safely by email and he'd be in a position to drop the camera-ready copy round to me for a final check by next weekend.

There is one small snag, which is that in order to get the book to a round number of pages, it's necessary to cut a page of text. I decided that Arthur Ramsbottom should be the one to determine what we should ditch, and rang him for a decision. He sounded quite devastated when I told him the purpose of my call. "I'll have to think about it and get back to you," he said. "It's heartbreaking to have to lose any of it." I felt almost as though I was asking which of his relatives to select for summary execution.

Eventually I got a call back at twenty past eleven. Arthur advised me, with a heavy heart, that of a shortlist of three, he felt he had no choice but to bin the hysterical account of the matins service in June 1972 when The Choir Were Given The Wrong Anthem Books.

Thus mercifully preserving for posterity two unmissable nuggets from the choir's past: the uproarious tale of May 1979, when Angela Spilsbury Got A Piece Of Incense Ash Lodged In Her Cassock, and the sidesplitting story of August 1988 when Mr Enderby The Visiting Organist Had To Interrupt The Friday Night Practice To Ask The Unofficial Evening Churchyard Maintenance Party To Turn Off The Lawn Mower.

Sunday 10th August

August at St Basil's traditionally sees the lousiest attendances of the year, the number of tourists who decide to include us as part of their itinerary being far exceeded by the number of regulars who are on holiday or for whom the summer heat makes it too much of an effort to get out of bed on a Sunday morning. It certainly was an absolute scorcher today. But although the congregation was rather poor, the singing was excellent and Mike's organ playing was superb. And certainly good enough for him to avoid censure, even from Hazel Ledworthy, for refusing to robe, playing the service in an open-necked polo shirt and swimshorts, and choosing as his closing voluntary *Variations On Nice One Cyril.* I could swear I overheard Marjorie Plumtree asking him if he could play it at her mother's funeral on Wednesday.

Afterwards, Brian and Rachel extended an invitation to the whole choir to a barbecue in their garden next Saturday night. Also present will be the French couple who hosted them during last August's trip to St Pierre and who are staying with them for the whole of this week. Alison confirmed that she would be there, together with Matthew and Zoe. "We came up with a great idea to get more money for the vestry fund, actually," said Matthew as we walked away afterwards.

"How?" I queried.

"Simple," he said. "Anybody who wants to entertain us afterwards can do so but they have to pay a fee."

I gently reminded him that it was customary for people to pay fees to be entertained, not do the entertaining.

Alison, however, told me that it was actually her suggestion. "Just think," she said. "Most people who stand up and do comic turns and songs at these events do it primarily for their own satisfaction. This way if we get bored out of our skulls listening to it, we do at least know that some money's gone somewhere useful."

I still had my doubts, and Rachel was also a little uneasy. But Brian came up with an excellent compromise. "What about a competition?" he suggested. "I'll go and buy a bottle of bubbly, everyone enters who wants to, they all pay an entry fee, we take a vote on who was the best, and that person wins the booze." Brilliant.

During the evening I managed to speak to most of the other choir members on the phone and tell them what was planned. Almost everyone was very much up for it and sportingly said they'd provide entertainment of some description. Craig says he has a hilarious skit on the *Orpheus In The Underworld* cancan using underground stations, Arthur Ramsbottom will have the opportunity after all to tell the story of the erroneous anthem books, and Irving Cattermole has a shaggy-dog story involving a policeman's helmet and an overripe Ugli fruit. Or vice versa.

The only negative note came from Cora, who said she felt it was the height of degradation for individual choir members to stand up and perform knowing that their work was being analysed, nobody in the choir was sufficiently qualified to comment on the merits of the work of another, and accordingly she did not feel she could be seen to risk compromising her status in an arena that was inappropriate and devoid of capacity for dispassionate and unbiased appraisal of her singing ability. Yet I'm sure there was no mention of a booby prize.

Saturday 16th August

After a lovely but very late night with Katie, taking advantage of a Friday evening with no choir practice, I could have stayed in bed most of the morning. But I was forced out of my slumbers much earlier than I would have liked by Roger Endacott, hand-delivering to me a package which was found to contain the complete text of the choir history in camera-ready form, with cover picture and blurb. Even in the Land of Nod there seems to be no escape from the mediocre musings of A. Ramsbottom Esq.

I tried my best to get back to sleep but my dozing was interrupted by a phone call from Rachel, which I might easily have missed if I'd not been woken by Roger Endacott. She told me that Serge and Jacqueline, who put her and Brian up last August, had unexpectedly brought with them their twelve-year-old grandson Antoine, and asked if I could do her a favour by keeping an eye on him at tonight's party to enable his grandparents to relax and mingle with the other guests. It sounded a reasonable request. But then at that stage I'd not met him.

It was another tremendously hot day. Neither Katie nor I are beach bums, nor are we particularly into sunbathing, so we settled instead for a relaxing afternoon in the beer garden of the Three Horseshoes. We really had no wish to change out of our T-shirts and shorts into smarter attire and drag ourselves out this evening, and if I'd not promised to help Rachel I would have been tempted to give the whole thing a miss. But we dutifully went home, changed, and presented ourselves at Brian and Rachel's as arranged. I remembered Serge and Jacqueline from last year, and knew them to be a quite delightful couple. Which was more than could be said for Antoine whose first act of friendly welcome was to squirt a lemon juice squeezer straight at Katie and me. Fortunately the juice wiped off her black leather platform mules quite easily, but the liquid hit my trousers in a particularly awkward place and the damp cloth Rachel rigorously applied to it only served to make the problem worse. Whilst I busied myself collecting entry money for the entertainment, Antoine insisted on following me around, firing a toy gun at me as he went, and he thought it the height of hilarity, having watched me painstakingly draw up a timetable for the entertainment on Brian's laptop, to press a key which instantly resulted in the loss not only of my work but what looked like two months' worth of Brian's accounts spreadsheets. It was only my brandishing Brian's *Times* colour supplement just within reach that caused him to dash from the room faster than one could say Eurosceptic.

Because it was such a beautiful evening, we were able to eat in the garden using a number of tables Brian had borrowed from the church hall earlier in the day. The food was delicious and, thanks to Antoine's attentions transferring to Rachel's long-suffering pet dog Rufus, Katie and I were able to enjoy our dinner in peace. We sat with our hosts and their French guests; Katie's French was excellent and she spent some time talking to Serge in his native tongue, translating her questions and his responses for the benefit of the rest of us. Serge told us that he was a great accordion enthusiast and I asked if he might play a little for us at the end of the evening. He was delighted to agree.

In fact, so relaxed and content was I that when I saw that Cora had arrived, I made a point of going over to her table to say hallo and thank her for coming, despite her refusal to take part in the entertainment. For once I felt quite sorry for her.

"Actually," she said, "I've had a change of heart. I decided I was being a bit churlish and so I would like to take part after all. If you could slot me in at the end I'd be so pleased." And she pledged a cash sum representing double the official entry fee.

At that moment I heard an anguished canine yelp from the corner of the garden, and perceived Antoine hurrying in my direction, with a broad grin on his face, evidently delighted that the wretched Rufus had become his latest victim. Before I could utter a word of censure or protest, Antoine had planted himself under the table at which Cora and I were sitting, presumably anticipating that the dog might seek some form of revenge. By now, the novelty of Antoine's juvenile excesses had rather worn off, and angry that my little conversation with Cora had been

115

interrupted in this way, I aimed a frustrated kick at the crouching figure beneath our feet. I really did not mean to connect, but the combination of my rather alcoholic afternoon and my annoyance at his latest escapade must have affected me more than I realised, for the toe of my Doc Marten shoe scored a direct hit on the very part of his nether regions where it might have been expected to do him the most good. At once his mischievous grin gave way to an ear-splitting howl and I was all ready to offer an unqualified apology, assemble a powerful legal team to defend me against charges of common assault and child cruelty, and reach for my chequebook with a view to offering a generous out-of-court payment in full and final settlement of any action for short-term pain, medium-term physical discomfort, long-term damage to feelings and lifelong psychological torment. Before I could do any of these things, however, he sprang up, pointed his finger at the innocent and totally perplexed Cora, and said to her "Lady you kick me. I get back at you. You see!" He was gone before either Cora or I had had the chance to explain what had actually happened.

Fortunately things calmed down thereafter, and by nine thirty we were ready to start the competition in Brian and Rachel's spacious drawing room. We proceeded to hear a variety of acts ranging from the well executed and enjoyable to the frankly painful. We all enjoyed Alison and Matthew's flute and piano duet, Mike Pitheavlis' cello solo and Margaret Pardew's clarinet duet with her younger sister, but just as I predicted, Arthur's anthem book story and Irving Cattermole's overripe policeman's helmet joke bored the pants off everybody, while Craig Dumbleton's cancan version of the London Underground began to run out of steam shortly before Boston Manor and was eventually derailed just after pulling out of Belsize Park. Then it was Cora's turn. I should have suspected the worst when I saw Antoine helping himself to an extremely large portion of gooey trifle but not actually eating any of it. However I suspected nothing amiss as she took centre stage; I simply sat back and groaned inwardly as she struggled through the longest and slowest operatic aria I had ever heard. As she reached the alleged climax – I thought I saw one or two fingers poised for earhole blocking – I saw Antoine's hand upraised. Seconds later, a paper-plateful of trifle was seen to shoot into the air, and moments after take-off made an explosive crash-landing right in the middle of Cora's face, precipitating an avalanche of mixed whipped cream, single cream and custard down her neck and on to her black sequined evening dress, while fragments of sponge and jelly were left scattered around the upper reaches and nursery slopes. Whether the audience thought it was pre-planned or not I don't know, but it brought the biggest laugh of the evening. Not from Cora, needless to say, who seconds later was demanding suitable retribution for the perpetrator

which if she had her way would consist of an order for immediate deportation, or, if that proved an unacceptable interference with the offender's rights under the European Convention, forcing him hang from the market cross whilst being pelted with rancid watermelons.

Once order was restored and Jacqueline had diplomatically removed her grandson from the scene, Rachel stepped forward. I thought she was going to announce that there were no further entries and we were to start thinking about voting, but instead she announced "To bring our entertainment to a close tonight, Serge, one of our guests, is going to play for us on the accordion."

The events of the past few minutes were quite forgotten as we sat through five minutes of Serge's quite exquisite French music making. There was no mistaking the pleasure on the faces of everybody as they listened, or the sincerity of the loud applause as he finished. And it was no surprise whatsoever when he was voted the runaway winner and gratefully accepted a bottle of champagne. Nobody seemed to mind that he had not actually entered the competition in the first place.

That is, except Cora, who proceeded to announce that in view of this latest outrageous development she would not be lending her facilities to any other choir event this year, and would be seeking recompense out of the monies raised tonight to dry-clean or replace her soiled clothing. I suspect she might have promised to apply even tougher sanctions, had she not been quite so preoccupied with major site clearance work. Indeed I was quite sure that shortly afterwards I witnessed Matthew and Zoe together thumbing through the Yellow Pages seeking the services of a local skip hire firm.

As for Antoine, his future is assured. Either as Somerset county cricket team's leading fast bowler or opera critic for the *New Statesman*.

Sunday 17th August

Tripplehorn's penultimate Sunday away. Today we had the dubious privilege of Arnold Petherbridge at the organ. Somehow he did manage to stay awake throughout the proceedings and in fact so keen was he to demonstrate his ability to anticipate what was coming that the offertory hymn was played immediately before the Gospel, the communion hymn was played at the offertory, and the recessional hymn was played over as pleasing background muzak while the vicar as part of the appeal from the local homeless hostel sought unwanted tins of grapefruit segments and creamed rice pudding.

Meanwhile, the gradual hymn was reported missing and rumoured to be on a plane bound for Guadeloupe.

Afterwards Raymond Mislingford, the chairman of the Events Committee of the PCC, came into the vestry to speak to the choir. Apologising for the short notice, he asked us if we're available next (Bank Holiday) weekend, to sing for an hour or so on Sunday late morning and again in the afternoon, to form an additional part of our church's contribution to the arts festival which is running in the town from tomorrow until Bank Holiday Monday. The church is apparently already laying on a number of events during the course of the festival including concerts, cream teas and floral displays, and the stairs leading up to the minstrels' gallery have also been repaired, making that area accessible for the first time for over a century. The whole thing is being coordinated by the PCC who assumed that with Tripplehorn absent there'd be no possibility of choir involvement. But in just the last few days the vicar has managed to persuade a musical friend and apparently extremely talented organist, Miles Shapcott who lives in Cheshire but is holidaying here for a fortnight, to lead us for this event. He has already agreed to rehearse with us on Friday and play the organ for next Sunday morning's service. Moreover, if we do take part, we will get a small fee which, together with donations we hope will be made by those who come in to listen to us, can all be added to the vestry fund.

A surprising number of choir members volunteered. Irving Cattermole, however, raised a legitimate and important point. "If we've only got one evening's rehearsal with the guy," he said, "how on earth are we meant to put two hours' worth of music together?"

"Oh, there's no difficulty with your doing the same one hour programme twice," Raymond Mislingford replied. "Or a half hour programme four times, for that matter. It's very informal. The expectation is that visitors will wander round the church, enjoy the displays, have a bit of refreshment, or just relax, with your music effectively as a nice additional touch. I don't think anyone's expecting Royal Festival Hall standards of performance."

And just as well, if besides being presented with a challenging menu of music to be performed we're to have our concentration levels tested to the limit by our audience members sitting in the front row slurping their 50p cups of tea and champing at crumbly slices of 75p Victoria sponge cake.

Friday 22nd August

Was hoping for just a quick runthrough with Mr Shapcott and then home. But not a bit of it. Either heedless or ignorant of Raymond Mislingford's concept of the choral contribution, he went through each piece for our two slots on Sunday in quite painful detail. "If we've got an audience, and we're expecting them to give us a donation, we need to be reasonably professional about it," he said. I suppose somebody ought to have gently pointed out to him that most of the audience we are likely to get wouldn't know their sforzandos from their volti subitos and who if asked what the

Latin word "hominibus" meant in English would hazard a guess that it was a vehicle used for the transportation of gardening equipment.

And as we laboured through *Sing We Merrily Unto God* for the umpteenth time, I decided that if we were asked to blow up the trumpet in the new moon once more, I'd plead a shortage of gunpowder. Or a severe case of chapped lips.

Sunday 24th August

The service started half an hour early this morning, the idea being that refreshments would be served in the church rather than in the hall, and we would sing some of our party pieces to the congregation, thereby assuring us of a semi-captive audience. We did at least reap some of the benefits of the rather arduous choir practice on Friday, singing better than we had done for some weeks, although the thought that we would have to sing Amner's *Come Let's Rejoice* twice more today, having sung it five and a half times barely 36 hours previously, did make me wonder if we ought to commission another anthem to complement it. Entitled *Come Let's Chill Out.*

As part of the church's contribution to the festival, we had a guest preacher this morning, a bishop from Brazil named Miguel Constantia. It was gratifying to see how well supported he was, with one of the best summer congregations I've ever seen at St Basil's. He was direct and forthright in his approach. "As choir members, you are this church's shop window," he told us before the service. "You must show how much God means to you through the leading part you play in the life and worship of the church." I thought how ironic it was that citizens of countries that weren't even discovered when Christianity came to England should now feel moved to come here to impart the Christian message. And when he spoke of the hardships and privations that church members suffered on his continent I will admit that I felt quite ashamed about our own complacent attitude to our freedom to worship. It was no surprise when following his invitation to us to meet with him to talk more about Christianity in his own country while partaking of coffee and home-made cake, many of the congregation readily went forward to speak to him, apparently taking no notice of the music we were providing at the same time. The upshot was that we decided to stop our recital until we had a few more listeners, and as a result we finished not at twelve as expected but twenty to one, in front of an audience of precisely four. Of these, I caught three glancing surreptitiously at their watches from twelve twenty onwards, while the fourth proceeded in a businesslike and single-minded fashion with a close forensic examination of the content of his left nostril. Which while less immediately distracting to the eye than slices of Mildred Fossington's iced bara brith looked a good deal less appetising.

We were due to start back again at two thirty but with the hot summer sun shining brilliantly outside and visions of an ice-cold fruit-filled Pimms in the garden of the Three Horseshoes I asked if we could resume a little later. Fortunately most of the choir agreed with me, and Joan Trumpington, who had prepared a typed schedule of the day's events, assured us that there would be no difficulty whatsoever about a later start. Eventually we agreed on three fifteen. Of course I should have realised, having seen her programme notes stating that donations from our singing were going to the "Vesty fund," that any assurance by Joan Trumpington had to be taken with more pinches of salt than Moby Dick's Saturday night takeaway. And it should not have surprised me in the least that ten past three saw us enter the church to find three scruffily dressed men in their twenties unpacking a variety of percussion equipment and placing it upon a crudely erected rostrum at the top end of the nave. I was somewhat nervous about confronting any of them, but Cora had no such reservations, marching up to the tallest and most formidably built individual in the trio and demanding to know what was going on.

"We've got the church for the next hour," he replied. "Drumming It Easy."

"I dare say you are," Cora Willoughby-Smith put in. "But not in this church please. This is a religious building, not the Earl Grey Whistle Test."

"You don't understand, man," one of the other band members piped up. With his open-toed sandals and home-rolled cigarette – I assume of tobacco, but couldn't be certain – hanging out of one corner of his mouth he looked and sounded like an exhibit from a 1960's theme museum. "That's what our band's called. Drumming It Easy. Triangle's my specialty but we do the works. Percussion. Drums, cymbals. Here, listen." He went over to one of the drumkits and would assuredly have deafened the whole choir with one bash of his stick, but discretion proved the better part of valour and wisely Cora conceded that there was just a chance that Joan Trumpington might have made a mistake. Which did not make sitting listening to a sample selection of their percussion so-called music, in front of an infuriatingly sizeable and enthusiastic audience, any more enjoyable. I honestly think I'd heard more meaningful and aesthetically pleasing sounds from my dustbin lid crashing against my garden fence in last winter's gales.

It wasn't until gone four o'clock that we finally began our vocal selection and as if by magic the majority of the audience disappeared, leaving just five hardy souls listening to the pieces we had practised so painstakingly on Friday night. As we were getting close to the end, however, I noticed a group of four come in, two of whom were at least a generation younger than anybody else who had so far listened to the choir today. They sat down towards the back and appeared to enjoy our music so much that I was quite disappointed that they hadn't had the chance to hear more of what we'd had to offer. Afterwards I went over and said as much to them, and to my surprise the older woman replied in a broad American accent. "Don't worry a bit," she said. "It was just so great to hear even a tiny bit of singing. I just wish we had something like that back home. Or a church as lovely as this."

It turned out they were all visitors from Chicago and were touring southern England, taking a particular interest in the churches. The older woman introduced herself to me as Linda and a moment later I was shaking hands not only with her but her husband Clint, her son Adam and her daughter-in-law Stacey. "I don't suppose you do conducted tours of this church, do you?" Clint enquired.

I shook my head sadly. I had asked exactly the same question of Ken Foulkes earlier today, and he'd told me that although two summers ago we had done a series of experimental tours at weekends, the take-up had been so poor that we'd decided to do away with them.

"Well, listen," said Clint, producing a substantial wadge of cash from his wallet. "I see from your programme notes that you need some money for vesties, whatever those are. If you could see your way to giving us a tour of this great building, I'll keep you in vesties for however long you need."

I could hardly believe that Joan Trumpington's latest attack of maladministration was actually likely to make us some money, but I was certainly not going to throw up such a fantastic opportunity and I decided to give it a go. My knowledge of the architecture of St Basil's was sadly limited despite my choir membership, but I remembered that on the bookstall at the back of the building there was a little church guidebook, written by one Abraham Meade-Ratchett. Helped by occasional surreptitious glances at this masterpiece of dry humourless church history, guaranteed to send a further generation of would-be students of architecture into courses in media studies or the waiting rooms of the next *Pop Idol* auditions, I suddenly became a positive authority on flying buttresses, bas-reliefs and stiff-leafed corbels. I laced this delicate historical detail with some anecdotes of choir history, a few of which were lifted from the hypnotic prose of Arthur Ramsbottom, and rather more of which were the products of my own imagination. After all, I reasoned to my protesting conscience, I can't see Clint going right through his collection of old videos to verify my assertion that the choir were used as extras in three early Agatha Christie films, any more than I can visualise Linda thumbing through any biographical work on Noel Coward to see which early work of his was conceived during his stint as a choirboy at St Basil's under the tyrannic tutelage of Doctor Cyrus Tregantle.

"It's been a great tour," said Adam as I brought proceedings to a close after an hour. "Any chance of just visiting the minstrels' gallery before we go?"

So absorbed had I been in my somewhat embellished account of choir activity over the past century that I had quite forgotten the gallery was open. Pocketing the money which Clint now handed to me, I led my four new friends to the door giving access to the recently repaired staircase. To my disappointment I saw a large CLOSED sign attached to it. Nonetheless, I tried the handle, the door opened, and ten minutes later, after a long climb up steep and winding steps that tested our nerves as well as our lungs, the five of us were standing looking out across the church from on high. It was a splendid spectacle. From Meade-Ratchett's book I became aware that there is a fine acoustic from the gallery, and I decided to amuse my audience by testing it, using some plainchant that we had performed earlier in our recital. To see the reaction of Clint and Linda, one would think that they had just been serenaded by Frank Sinatra, and seconds later a further supply of banknotes was pressed into my grateful hands. At their suggestion, we bowed our heads for a few moments of silent prayer and thanksgiving, then prepared to go. All I had to do was lead them back down the stairs and a highly successful day's fundraising would have been complete. Slowly we made our way back down the steep staircase. As we neared the bottom, I heard a bang, the lights illuminating the steps went out, and a moment later I was aware of the sound of receding footsteps. One unsuccessful pull at the door a moment later confirmed my worst fears.

I suppose we could be said to have made the best of a bad job, once it became clear that every single person connected with the church whose telephone number I had logged into my mobile phone was either unable or unwilling to answer it. During the three quarters of an hour that we allowed for those with answering machines to get back to me, I got to know my fellow prisoners very well, from Clint's obsession with his local baseball team, the Railton Road Rockers, to Adam and Stacey's window cleaner's first tentative steps towards gender reassignment. For my part, I somehow managed to secure orders for four signed copies of Arthur Ramsbottom's book. And so confident was my raconteuring becoming, that I was even beginning to convince myself of the truth of my hastily conceived story about Albert Pulleyblank, the St Basil's choir ghost who appears every 29th February and sits in the choirstalls singing selected snatches of Noble in B minor.

A deafening silence from my mobile after those 45 minutes, however, meant that more drastic measures were called for if we were to emerge from our incarceration with both our bodies and our senses intact. Having said that, I do feel that it was somewhat churlish of the vicar, citing my allowing visitors into the gallery after 5pm in clear defiance of the CLOSED sign, to insist on our making inroads into the vestry fund to compensate the PCC: firstly for the new lock that will be needed after Adam had used some dubiously acquired skills to break the pre-existing one, and secondly for the third-to-bottom step which had given way in the sudden darkness under the pressure of Linda's size seven and a half chunky-soled pink trainers.

As we made our way out of the church, I felt that the least I could do was offer hospitality to my erstwhile fellow prisoners. "I think not, thank you," Clint replied, politely but somewhat coolly. "We really ought to be getting on."

Not that I can really say I blame them. After being stuck inside St Basil's church for far longer than their hectic schedule realistically permitted, I can quite understand their wanting to place as many miles between themselves and the building, with its attendant army of vesties, as was humanly possible.

I was still unwinding two hours later, reflecting that my actions had now twice in eight days seen money destined for the vestry fund being thrown away, when the phone rang. It was Joan Trumpington.

"I gather I locked you in the minstrels' gallery," she said. "I am sorry. But it was after five o'clock and the CLOSED sign was up. And I did think everyone had gone home."

I asked her if my plainchant recital might not have given her the slightest clue that not everyone had in fact gone home.

"Oh, I never heard that," she said. "You must have been singing into my bad ear."

I agreed that that had to be a distinct possibility.

"Anyway," she said, "I hope you got out all right."

I just managed to resist the temptation to tell her that as a matter of fact I was still stuck up there, her phone call having jerked me out of a state of supreme ecstasy induced by a combination of inhalation of the substance being puffed by Drumming It Easy's chief triangle biffer, and the sound of the ghostly figure of Albert Pulleyblank reeling off his third refrain of *Ging Gang Gooly*.

Sunday 31st August

Arrived at church feeling refreshed after a few lovely days away with Katie, We were virtually a full house again this morning. Ruth Hartnell was back, and got down to business straight away, producing a formidable rehearsal schedule for the play in early December. Tripplehorn was also back, predictably smirking as we filled him in on

124

the shortcomings of the stand-ins. After the service, he announced that in the course of an organists' summer school he had attended, he had managed to secure the services of one Andrew Sentence to do a Bring And Sing day for us in aid of the vestry fund. The object of the day is to learn a complete choral work, starting from scratch first thing in the morning and giving a performance before a paying audience in the evening. The event is open to everybody, not just us, but all choir members will in fact be expected to participate.

After our experiences with Melvyn Samlesbury in May, it wasn't surprising that the news was not greeted with huge enthusiasm. However, Tripplehorn hastened to point out that Andy, as he called him, has led many of these events in the past, and all have been hugely successful. That is the good news. The bad news, in a sense, is that his schedule for the autumn is so tight that the only day he can offer us is September 20th, less than three weeks away. But it's take it or leave it. Andy will start rehearsing with us at 9.30am promptly, spending the morning note-bashing with those who have never seen the piece before, and the afternoon putting the final polish on it. The expectation is that although we as choir members should be in attendance all day to give a good lead to the singing, it will be quite in order for outsiders who are familiar with the work to rehearse in the afternoon only. We will then give a proper performance to paying customers at 7.30pm. Vestry money will be raised through fees for taking part, admission charges for watching the performance, and the sale of refreshments during the breaks.

"What piece will we be doing?" Rachel enquired.

"He gave us quite a wide choice," said Tripplehorn. "Durufle Requiem, Durufle Requiem or......Durufle Requiem. He said he's always wanted to do that piece in the context of a Bring And Sing day. And I have to say I agree it's a splendid selection. A piece of intense, extraordinarily moving writing, very appropriate and popular in the context of funeral and All Souls masses, linking the timeless beauty of medieval plainchant with the more flexible contemporary genre to make it an accessible and deeply spiritual musical experience."

"Is that the only reason you like it?" Lesley asked him.

"Oh yes," said Tripplehorn. "That, and the fact that if we do it he'll give us a 50 per cent discount off his bill."

Having sung the Durufle myself, with two or three different choirs, I had no particular difficulty with it. Indeed, most people seemed happy enough. Not Irving Cattermole, obviously. I heard him muttering to Henry Peasgood "If anyone plays that at my funeral, I won't bother to turn up." That certainly would be very bad news.

Friday 5th September

It was good to have a full choir practice again for the first time since the middle of July. Even better, Tripplehorn dug out Bruckner's *Christus Factus Est*, an extremely demanding piece which, as he said, "I wouldn't want to tackle in the absence of a full complement of choir members without a distress flare and a life jacket." I had never sung it at St Basil's but had performed it with at least two of my previous choirs and certainly ranked it in my top ten church anthems. It was thus to my delight that I found we were to be singing it this Sunday morning.

Ruth, having circulated the rehearsal schedule last Sunday, reminded us that play rehearsals were starting on Tuesday and would continue weekly until the performances themselves. Matthew was unwise enough to moan to his mother that that was quite a tall order, with *EastEnders* as well as football practice to fit into his hectic Tuesday night schedule. Ruth rounded angrily on him and said "You're really far too young to be watching far-fetched exploits of fractious manipulative adults in an endless round of tedious and selfish power struggles." Exactly. I can't imagine what he's doing at St Basil's.

We then went on to discuss the practical arrangements for the Durufle Requiem Bring And Sing day. Tripplehorn has managed to get the PCC at its meeting this week to finance, print and circulate posters advertising the event throughout the town. Unwilling, as usual, to take any of the work on himself, it seemed he had persuaded two PCC members, Clive Treadwell and Victor Rattigan, to do the work rather than me. I whispered to Lesley that I was quite touched that he had had the sensitivity and decency to spread the responsibility about the church community and refrain from placing yet another burden on my overworked shoulders. "Oh, he would have done," said Lesley, "but he couldn't get hold of you on Tuesday night and assumed your answering machine was on the blink."

There was a catch, of course. Tripplehorn had agreed to do an interview with the local rag first thing on Sunday morning, but, on the most feeble of pretexts – a party on Saturday night in London that he's afraid he won't have properly slept off by the time the reporter comes round – he wants someone else to do it, and had volunteered me. This regardless of the fact that, as Ruth had told me a couple of months back, the majority of the reporters on the paper are a bunch of brainless imbeciles. Not to mention that it will mean losing one of my two precious lie-ins of the week.

"One other thing," Tripplehorn said to us as we considered the practical aspects of the day. "Even though most of you know the music, you are expected to be there for the whole day so we can provide a lead to those who won't know it. Andy Sentence is preparing some notes on the dynamics and speeds for the Durufle which he wants us to look at before the day."

I couldn't resist adding "Is that what they call handing down a Sentence?" But for all the response I got, I might have been addressing a room full of marinated aubergines.

Sunday 7th September
Arrived at St Basil's at a quarter to nine for my meeting with Terry Stacey, the only available reporter that morning. He was the one who had asked for this early slot, explaining he had numerous other events to cover that day of major global importance, starting with the Hinkley Farm Ploughing Match and ending with the St Augustine's Park Women's Institute sponsored baby bootee knitting contest. Yet it wasn't until eleven minutes past nine that a bearded scruffy individual, dressed in T-shirt, faded jeans and even more faded trainers, ambled towards me and introduced himself. Having immediately demonstrated the depth of his commitment to skilful and sensitive reportage of local religious affairs by pointing to the church and saying "I've never really got involved in all that business since Sunday School" he then compounded his proud ignorance of matters spiritual by a feeble joke involving Pontius Pilate and the flight into Egypt which if I'd heard once I had heard a hundred times, and a number of other statements that at once made Zoe Sparkes look like a potential Masters level Bible scholar. We then moved on to talk about my fundraising activities, and here things did look up as I recounted some of the more comical aspects of the year so far, only to go seriously downhill again as I endeavoured to tell him about our Durufle day on Saturday week. "Remind me about Durufle," said Terry. "I always believed that to be a cheese pudding, but doubtless you'll put me right." I can only guess he was trying to be funny but having regaled me with his "favourite piece of graffiti – JESUS SAVES, BUT BECKHAM KNOCKS IN THE REBOUND" I decided I really could not take anything for granted.

Having discussed the format of the day and the need for as many local singers as possible to support it, we were able to draw the interview to a close, just five minutes or so before I was due at church for the morning service. I was about to bid farewell to Terry when he said "Right. If you don't mind hanging on a few moments longer, the photographer should be here any second."

This was the first I'd heard that I was expected to pose for a photo. Had I known, I might have bothered to dress more smartly for the occasion and would have popped into Hair Today for a quick trim yesterday afternoon.

After kicking my heels for ten minutes, I was about to tell Terry I couldn't wait any longer, when a sweaty-palmed shaven-headed youth sporting tattoos on both arms and a ring dangling from his right ear lobe wandered up to me and announced himself as Rob, the cameraman. Terry went off, probably to the nearest eaterie for a double helping of Duruflé with tangy tropical pineapple topping, leaving me in Rob's less than pristine hands. Rob first of all insisted on driving me to this "really cool church just out of town" and then got me to pose with my dog-eared copy of the Requiem in at least twenty different places and adopting a variety of bodily postures that even the most fanatical devotees of yoga would dismiss as contrary to one's Geneva Convention rights. By the time we'd finished, I'd discovered muscles amongst my anatomy that I had no idea existed. I had also missed the morning service which while causing no physical pain was extremely disappointing, particularly as it meant I'd missed Bruckner's *Christus Factus Est*. I suppose I should have been grateful that I hadn't had to endure any more of Terry's feeble attempts at ecclesiastical humour. But as I limped home in not inconsiderable discomfort, I reflected that rather than suffering in the way I had done over the last two hours I would almost have preferred to have spent the morning joining with El Tel in singing the schoolboy versions of *We Three Kings* or *John Brown's Body*. Or following the example of the eponymous hero of the latter song by doing a strawberry jam impersonation on the tarmac at Gatwick Airport.

Tuesday 9ᵗʰ September

Except for Jane, we were a full house for our play rehearsal tonight which took place, as all the play rehearsals will until the end of October, at Ruth's home. Naturally enough, everyone had completely forgotten all the moves Ruth had so painstakingly given us before she went on holiday. "Of course, it would have been helpful if you'd jotted down the moves in your copies in pencil," snapped Ruth after stopping scene 2 for the fifth time to reposition the cast. "Arthur, if I've told you once that the back of the settee marks the back of the stage, I've told you a hundred times. You managed to deliver your last two speeches from the car park." Though on the present showing that hardly seems to matter, bearing in mind that by the time he comes on that is probably where most of the audience will be headed for anyway.

As we were getting ready to pack up, Ruth dropped her bombshell. "I want the first fifteen pages done from memory next Tuesday night," she said. "It really isn't too early. Besides which, I'm a firm believer that you can't possibly act the part properly and engage appropriately with your audience unless the book is out of your hands."

She obviously hadn't seen Angus Wintergreen at the nearby village panto two Januarys ago filling in on the night for the three members of the cast who'd gone sick. Even having to clasp a script he'd never seen before he still brought to bear more thespian skills in his portrayal of Able Seaman Sonny Sovert'yardarm, the village policeman Copper Loadathis, and a shipwrecked Japanese golfer Ho Lin Wun, than the rest of the cast were able to do after nine months' rehearsal.

Friday 12th September

As I rehearsed some very unexciting music at choir tonight, I felt doubly annoyed at missing church last Sunday morning. Tripplehorn did absolutely nothing to assuage these negative feelings, telling me that he'd had another Bruckner anthem in mind for this Sunday morning, but had thought better of it, "in case you decide not to grace us with your presence again this time." I couldn't even counter his rubbing-my-nose-in-it routine by pointing to a decent photo and write-up in the paper, as because of "production difficulties" – which according to Ruth Hartnell could mean anything from a malfunctioning stapling machine in the front office to the assistant deputy production editor's sister's first cousin's beagle contracting hardpad – publication of this week's edition has been postponed to tomorrow morning.

Tripplehorn asked how much interest had been taken in the Bring And Sing event, which is now just eight days away. The response was not encouraging. Although Tripplehorn boasted, with I thought quite unwarranted smugness, that he had given it very considerable coverage at a function he had attended on Wednesday evening, nobody else was able to volunteer a single occasion on which they had mentioned it to other people. Unless the newspaper publicity generates a significant number of takers, we as a choir may well be singing to ourselves throughout next Saturday. And not the whole choir either. Eileen Crosby has a long-standing engagement. Craig Dumbleton has an unavoidable winter season planning meeting for the Sornies, also known as the Southern Railway Nostalgia Enthusiasts, in the Snug Bar of the Locomotive Arms, Rainham, at midday. And Irving Cattermole didn't even bother to invent an excuse.

Fortunately, there was another vestry fundraising suggestion on the table tonight. Alison and Matthew have between them offered to organise a games evening at the end of October. With collapsing ping-pong tables and triple portions of chips and mushy peas still fresh in the mind, I reckon I could have been forgiven for looking more than a little askance at the prospect.

"It's not what you're thinking," said Alison, having seen my jaw drop faster than the price of shares in hosepipes during the operational period of a drought order. "We thought we'd play some of the famous panel games like *Many A Slip, I'm Sorry I Haven't A Clue, Just A Minute* and so on. Just leave it to us. We'll do all the legwork. No prizes for the winners, no teams as such. Choir members and their friends invited. Just a bit of relaxing fun."

Then again, as Brian reminded me, that's what they said the Women's Monthly Fellowship Beetle Drive would be. The same Beetle Drive that saw the two top tables overturned, three teacups smashed, and the caller refusing to leave the building without a police escort.

Sunday 14th September

Having felt really rather bad about the fact that our choirmaster had been the only one out of all of us, myself included, to publicise the Bring And Sing event during the past week, I decided to forgo my lie-in for the second Sunday morning running and not only buttonhole every member of the congregation with details of the event as they came into church, but to do the same with those coming out of the 8am service. I don't know whether there was a higher proportion of hung-over congregation members than average this morning, but all I can say is that I have never felt such a close or sympathetic affinity with double-glazing salesmen, door-to-door encyclopedia merchants, or those standing with clipboards in the pouring rain outside the Shire Hall asking office workers to give up part of their hard-earned lunch hour to nominate their favourite brand of liquid carpet stain remover.

As I trudged into the vestry, having failed to generate a commitment from anybody, I happened to meet Lesley and explained what I'd been doing. She asked me why and I told her I was concerned Tripplehorn was the only person who seemed to have made any effort with the publicity.

"I wouldn't let that Wednesday evening business get on your conscience too much," she said. "First, it was only a party at Mike Pitheavlis' place. And what he actually said that anyone who went within a hundred miles of the event had to be one Dandy short of a magazine rack."

Before the service this morning we were duly presented with Andy Sentence's notes for the Bring And Sing. The guy obviously fancies himself as a bit of a wag, his notes on dynamics interspersed with gratuitous comments of his own on the piece in general, such as "Bar 15 – cheesy or what!......bar 28 – Sopranos, if I hear you being drowned by the tenors don't expect me to call in the RNLI.... bar 67 – the Caerleon Mixed Voice Harmonists never got this right so it'll be one up to you if you can…" And so on.

We sang three of the Durufle numbers during the service this morning, partly as an appetiser for the punters for next Saturday, and partly as rehearsal. It does strike me as slightly incongruous that we should be rehearsing in advance of a day of performing a work from scratch, but then again one can understand Andrew Sentence's desire to have a guaranteed minimum standard. Tripplehorn very annoyingly insisted on our staying on after the service this morning to go through the six numbers we had not performed during the service, giving us copious directions as far as dynamics and speed were concerned. "I don't know if it matters," said Henry Peasgood, "but half of your instructions seem to contradict all the ones that Mr Sentence gave on his handout."

"Oh, I know," said Tripplehorn. "I just wanted to see if you'd actually read the handout, that's all."

"So what do you want us to do, then?" I asked.

"Use your own judgment," he replied helpfully.

Afterwards he asked me if I'd seen my picture in the paper. I told him I'd looked everywhere on the entertainments and What's On pages but hadn't seen a sausage.

"Try page three," he said. "But don't take it too personally. They do say that today's news is the bottom of tomorrow's budgie cage."

That sounded ominous. And my worst fears were confirmed when Katie came round at lunchtime with a copy of the offending journal. I'm glad she saw the funny side. Nonetheless, I couldn't blame any cage-bird owner for wanting to retain the paper in question for posterity and looking for alternative sources of material for the base of his pet's residence having seen the photograph of me, complete with Durufle Requiem score, looking like the booby prize winner at the Market Deeping Annual Contortionists' Convention. Plus, directly underneath the photograph, the words "MOST WANTED BEAST" STRIKES AGAIN.

Katie suggested I laughed it off and forgot about it, but I decided I should register a formal complaint to the editor of the paper, and spoke to Tripplehorn who is going to make the complaint on my behalf. While I do agree with Katie that it is amusing in its way, I really am not sure I want to be labelled as a Most Wanted Beast, particularly if a reader does recognise me and tries to have me arrested. What makes the whole business all the more ridiculous is the fact that nowhere in the paper, and certainly not on the same page as the photo, can I find a story that explains why this beast is wanted so much. So when I am dragged by my overgrown right toenail into the back of a waiting police vehicle, I shall be none the wiser as to whether I have just been taken for a serial bag snatcher preying off elderly spinsters in the neighbourhood of the sheltered housing in Fowler Avenue or a sex attacker roaming the alleys around Queen Charlotte's Park. Or, of course, the subhuman fiend responsible for jamming the post office stamp machine by inserting a brace of out of date 5p pieces.

Tuesday 16th September

Our first play rehearsal without the books was not a success.

Things began promisingly enough, as Rachel and Ken, who one presumed had at least made a start on learning their lines, got through their first six speeches each with barely a squeak from Cynthia Halliday, the prompt. But by the end of page two, Cynthia was having to come in almost every other line. Three pages later it had turned into a one-woman show as Cynthia dutifully trotted out the lines in response to the hopelessly vacant looks on the faces of those who were supposed to be speaking them. A fairly predictable pattern had emerged: following the blank look, Cynthia would come in with the line, the person who was supposed to be saying it would make some fatuous retort such as "Of course" or "I knew that bit in the bath last night" and would then repeat the line after Cynthia, meaning that the play was effectively being performed twice, once by Cynthia and once by the rest of the cast. It rather reminded me of the Echo Torture Chamber I had had the misfortune to get lost in on the seafront at Lowestoft at the age of ten.

Cora Willoughby-Smith was not due on until page nine, and as we began the preceding page I noticed an expression on her face that I had seen a few times before at choir, meaning "Don't worry, this is all absolute rubbish but I am the one to save the show and turn this fiasco into a rip-roaring success." Despite the fact that it took an insufferably long time to claw our way through page eight, Cora was standing by, clearly desperate to get into the action, rather like a child waiting for permission to start unwrapping Christmas presents. Although I know Arthur Ramsbottom disagrees with me on this, I'm convinced that despite her fine words about the importance of this play as a community effort enabling participants to feel they are giving of themselves with no room for egotism or glory-seeking, she is in it purely for the praise she hopes, almost certainly in vain, will be lavished upon her.

As soon as her moment came, she leapt on to the set and delivered her first line, "'What on earth has been going on here, may I ask?'"

"Er – no," said the prompt.

"Excuse me?" Cora retorted dangerously.

"The line's not quite right," said Cynthia. "It should be 'May I ask what on earth has been going on here?'"

"Don't be ridiculous," Cora retorted icily. "I'm fully aware of what it says in the book. I happen to think that the way I've said the words produces more dramatic effect. Kindly reserve any future interruptions for occasions on which cast members do not come in with their line at all."

Suitably chastened, Cynthia sat back in her chair and kept silent, seemingly hardly daring to breathe, while Cora embarked on her lengthy ensuing monologue. It was not long, however, before fits of amnesia amongst other cast members threw Cynthia back into the limelight. Finally, halfway down page thirteen, there was a silence where Cora should have come in. Cynthia waited a good twenty seconds then tentatively offered the first couple of words. Immediately Cora exploded. "Have you not heard of the dramatic pause, woman!" she shrieked.

"Oh, that old one," whispered Matthew. Unfortunately he whispered it a little too loudly.

"Right, that does it," said Cora. "I've just about had enough of that woman's idiot interruptions and that wretched boy's facetious smile and his maddening asides. There really seems no point in carrying on as we are."

Thankfully, Ruth chipped in at this point. "I think perhaps we've gone as far as we reasonably can without books," she said. "I was going to call a halt anyway. Coffee, everyone?"

As we were leaving twenty minutes later, pleased to have been told that as Ruth is away we can have next Tuesday night off, I overheard Ruth say to Cora "Do try not to be too hard on Cynthia. Since she lost her husband earlier this year she really looks forward to getting out of the house in the evening, especially with the days getting shorter now."

"Well, that's all right then," Cora snapped back. "I gather they're advertising for night shelf-fillers at Tesco."

I rest my case.

Friday 19th September

At choir tonight Tripplehorn told me that as a result of my wish to complain about the "Most Wanted Beast" error he had now "had a quiet word" with the editor of the local paper with reference to those responsible. I suspect that it would be nearer the truth to suggest that in fact he had told the editor that his writers boasted the intellectual capacity and basic common sense of a syrup sponge pudding. But whatever approach was in fact adopted, it seems, according to our choirmaster, to have had its effect, inasmuch as the editor has promised to print a correction in today's edition. Also, by way of a goodwill gesture, he's agreed to give a further plug for the Bring And Sing day, even though this will mean having to lose the review of the town's punk band Cordite And Chips' gig in the Chesterfield Arms. "On that basis," Tripplehorn said confidently, "we might actually end up with a bigger crowd than we would have done originally."

I popped into my local convenience store on the way home to buy a paper. On page three there was a piece headed CORRECTION, apologising for the mistake in misplacing the photograph in last week's edition, and wishing to reassure readers that contrary to what was stated in the caption below, I was not in fact the Most Wanted Beast. At least, I think that was what the writer intended to say. It was I am sure human error that resulted in the word "not" being left out.

Still, Tripplehorn was probably right that the extra piece in today's paper will generate better numbers. If nothing else, on the strength of the following paragraph, which read "Turn to page 26 for more details about St Basil's exciting sinning event tomorrow."

Saturday 20th September

Arrived at nine to get the teas and coffees ready then joined with the other singers for a 9.30 start for the Bring And Sing day. There were disappointingly few people there; in fact, I counted just half a dozen singers in addition to the regular choir, plus Mike Pitheavlis who was accompanying us on the organ. I really did think, as did Andrew, that even though singers familiar with the piece had been told they needn't turn up till the afternoon, most people would still come for the morning session as well. I felt sorry for Ken and Brian who had arrived extra early on what was an unusually hot September day to organise seating space for many times the number that were actually present. Andrew Sentence duly appeared and introduced himself. He really was a very nice man, seemed extremely down to earth and obviously possessed a good sense of humour. Better still, following a last-minute mini-flurry of orders for drinks, he was more than happy to delay the start of the rehearsal to allow me to put away the vast unconsumed platefuls of biscuits before the resident St Basil's insect colony got to them.

We proceeded to enjoy an excellent morning's singing, and by lunchtime we had familiarised ourselves with the notes and so were able, as Andrew put it, "to start doing things with the music." Even though the attendance was distinctly disappointing, we consoled ourselves as we broke for lunch – a bring-your-own affair today – that maybe the majority of people were preferring to come along and watch the performance tonight rather than take part. However, as Katie and I munched our sandwiches on the bench outside the south porch, we couldn't help noticing vast numbers of people making their way down the path and into the church. By the time we'd taken our seats for the afternoon, I found myself in the company not only of the twenty or so singers of the morning but what looked like well in excess of forty others. And while it was nice to see what a great fillip this would be for the vestry fund, I became quite apprehensive as to the effect of this vast increase in numbers on the quality of the performance. My

134

worst fears were confirmed within thirty seconds of having started to sing again. I was now flanked on my right by a short man I guessed to be in his sixties, with a pronounced twitch, ruddy complexion, and more hair coming out of his ears than out of the top of his head, and on my left by an extremely large lady wearing huge surgical sandals and a faded flowery dress which looked as though it might last have seen service on the curtain rails of the local job centre. How she had got herself mixed up with the tenors I could not think, until I realised they were husband and wife and had just been too polite to ask if they could sit together rather than either side of me. But politeness was the least of my concerns when it became clear that the noise emanating from the two of them just in the first few bars of singing was enough not only to frighten the potential punters from their seats but to put the ants right off the Happy Shopper custard creams.

We staggered through the first couple of pages but in contrast to the excellent sound we'd been making this morning after going through that section at least ten times, this afternoon's effort could only be described as an embarrassment. Looking distinctly annoyed, Andrew Sentence stopped us and said "How many of you who have come for this afternoon have actually sung this piece before?"

About five or six hands were raised.

"May I ask, then," said Andrew, looking marginally agitated for the first time today, "why you weren't here this morning?"

"The paper didn't say anything about this morning," said a rather formidable-looking woman in the front row. She reminded me of my terrifying first-form history teacher, Miss MacSweeney. "It just said come along this afternoon for an afternoon's singing. Or sinning, to be precise."

"Well, which idiot said it was only the afternoon?" Andrew demanded. I looked across at Tripplehorn, who had joined the bass section, and noticed that he had suddenly become extremely interested in the dandruff that had set up camp on Agnes Stupplewick's plastic mackintosh. I might have guessed that he'd got Joan Trumpington to provide the additional information for yesterday's extra plug for the Bring And Sing day.

But there was nothing we could do about it. We would have to plough on. All the excellent work of the morning was completely undone as we grimly note-bashed our way through the score, spending several minutes on pages that had almost reached performance standard just a couple of hours previously. Andrew, who this morning had the exuberance and enthusiasm of a master craftsman absorbed in the enjoyment of his work, was by 4.30 – by which time we had not even got on to the Sanctus – registering all the exuberance and enthusiasm of the proverbial tempest-stricken expiring mallard. It did not help, of course, that less than a quarter or so of the assembled company had copies of the score, despite our making it clear that they should all bring one with them. And although we had made provision for possible shortages by rustling up a few spares before the day started, we now had a scene that brought back memories of school assemblies and the whole of form 1B crowding round Tomkins Minor, being the only person in the class to have remembered his *Schools Praise* book, for the purpose of singing the day's prescribed hymn either half a bar ahead of or two thirds of a bar behind Dr Bullivant on the piano.

By five thirty, when we were supposed to have finished, we still had three numbers to do including the tricky Lux Aeterna and Libera Me. Andrew suggested a five-minute break, called the regular choir members over and announced that he was not prepared to compromise his standards or his reputation by allowing the piece to be performed in the state it was. He added that either he would have to leave now and let somebody else conduct the concert, or he would stay rehearsing with us for however long it took. If the latter, he would require a substantial increase in his fee to take into account not only his time and trouble but the fact that he would be unable to go home in the interim and would require to partake of refreshment in the town.

Reluctantly, we felt we had no alternative but to slash the profits we had hoped to make from the day and allow him his additional fee.

By twenty to seven, when we finally concluded the *Agnus Dei* and Andrew pronounced himself "as satisfied as I can be" with what we had produced, my nerves were in rags, not just because of Andrew's demeanour but because of the antics of my neighbours. The curtain lady, who told me her name was Thelma Dolittle, had at least begun to run out of steam after an hour and a half, and there were even some blissful moments of silence from her cold-sore-festooned lips. Then, however, she began a series of spectacular coughing fits which reminded me in terms of volume, rhythm and aesthetic content of the noise made by the Volkswagen Polo belonging to my Wolverhampton Polytechnic housemate as he tried to start it in heavy snow. It was when she pronounced herself fit to continue to sing and attempted to combine her almost grotesque snatches at the correct notes with her unwitting motor vehicle engine impersonations that I realised the inaccuracy of the Requiem's vision of Hell as a pit of fire and really did begin to wish I had led a more saintly life. Her husband, who had introduced himself to me as Len, was not only equally musically incompetent but spent every spare moment providing me with a potted autobiography. At no stage, however, did he indicate having achieved any recognition for his singing skills. Unless, of course, he was too shy to admit to having just beaten his wife to the first prize in the Voice Most Resembling A Piece Of Paper Trying To Make Its Way Through A Faulty Fax Machine competition.

Finally, unable to take any more, I asked Len what singing experience he and his wife did have. "Oh, we're not singers," he said. "We just came to listen. But when everyone else seemed to be joining in it seemed rude not to as well."

I pointed out to him that the audience was supposed to come in the evening. "That's not what this week's paper said," Len responded. "It just said to come along in the afternoon for an enjoyable sing. I didn't realise we had to stay on to perform it tonight."

Was in two minds whether to advise Andrew that on the strength of that, we might be struggling to get an audience of nought for the performance but one look at his haggard features suggested that any intervention on my part would meet with a reaction as warm as the lower half of the brass monkey statue in Coldblast Square, Icy City, Northern Greenland. So I kept quiet, and hoped I'd be proved wrong.

I wasn't. At seven thirty, the advertised time of the performance, we had an audience of precisely eight.

As is so often the case, the lack of numbers caused any adrenalin surging about any of us to dry up more speedily than the kitchen staff at Burger King on a productivity bonus and we delivered a performance the standard of which was comparable to that at the start of this afternoon's rehearsal. I just couldn't wait for it to finish. I noticed that Andrew didn't stay around too long at the end, once he'd received his larger-than-expected cheque. What's more, I certainly can't see him coming back to St Basil's again in a hurry. Save to sign copies of his book which today's debacle had inspired him to write. *How To Reduce The Most Equable Conductor To A Bag Of Nerves In One Easy Lesson.*

Sunday 21st September

Although Tripplehorn can be ratty on a Sunday morning at the best of times, it really was quite a relief being under his proverbial baton this morning. I expected him to back Andrew to the hilt, but all he said was he had seen raspberry blancmanges with more solidity and robustness than Andrew had shown when the going had got tough towards the end.

During the service, the vicar mentioned that at next Sunday evening's Harvest supper, there will not be the usual entertainment. As part of the church's new initiative to reach out to the community, a special invitation is being extended to families, particularly those with babies and young children, in the hope that we can start to get a few younger people into our regular congregation. A large leaflet drop and local media campaign is under way with this end in mind. The service will be a shorter one than usual, starting at 5.30pm with supper served immediately afterwards at

6.15pm. Young children will be catered for and all the regular congregation and choir will be asked to introduce themselves to newcomers and make them feel welcome. If it is a success, the vicar said, there are resources available to start up a crèche. It'll certainly be a forward and innovative step for what is an increasingly elderly congregation, some of whom probably aren't sure what a crèche is. And if asked would hazard a guess that it was a road accident in Tunbridge Wells.

Friday 26th September

Tripplehorn phoned this morning. "Some good news," he said. "Tristan Chanctonbury's joining us for tonight's practice and the Harvest service."
The name meant nothing to me. "Who is he?" I asked.
"He was with us at St Basil's for a year or so in the 1980's," Tripplehorn replied. "He lives in Cambridge now but we've kept in touch ever since. He recently picked up an absolute gem at a car boot sale in Cambridge. Owner obviously didn't think it was anything special. It's a collection of hymn tunes by an 18th century composer, all signed, and bound by hand probably as long ago as the end of the 19th century. It's a very valuable piece. I've told Tristan all about the vestry fund and he's offered to let us have the bound collection so we can sell it for the fund. He'll be bringing it along tonight."

Tripplehorn mentioned he had one other matter to discuss with me tonight but so delighted was I by the news of Tristan Chanctonbury that I was really able to focus on very little else for the rest of the day. If we were able to raise a decent sum from the sale of the collection, it would certainly help to make up for the many recent disappointments and might actually put us a bit ahead of ourselves with just over a quarter of the year to go.

Tristan was a little late arriving at the practice tonight so I didn't get the chance to see him beforehand, but during a brief break in the practice, while Tripplehorn was preparing to distribute Sunday evening's anthem, I arranged to meet him in the pub afterwards to take delivery of the collection and agree a sum we should pay him for it. It was good to have him with us on the tenor line; while his best singing days are behind him, he still managed to improve on Arthur Ramsbottom's standard both by singing in tune and completing some passages in a dynamic other than double forte.

As soon as we finished the rehearsal, Tripplehorn asked to see me in private in the vestry. "It's rather embarrassing, this," he said, once we were alone together. I could see his complexion had reddened somewhat. "The fact is, I've had an official written complaint about you from one of the choir members. Hazel Ledworthy, to be precise."

I asked to see the letter and was frankly so amazed by the contents that I felt almost unable to take them in properly. The main thrust of her complaint was that I had pushed the vestry fundraising efforts too far, and that although I had only been in the choir five minutes I was already dictating the choir agenda. She resented my negative and aggressive body language in the face of those who for personal reasons did not wish to be as involved with the vestry fund as I was, or who lacked the musical competence required to carry off the various projects successfully, and she felt it was excessively presumptuous on my part to suggest that the choir should have to learn and sing my own compositions. She cited two occasions recently on which I had, uninvited, sung a section of anthem that was written for altos and basses only, saying this was symptomatic of my lack of regard for those who really were leading the musical aspect of the worship. She suggested that I should perhaps remember my place in the choir pecking order and respect the ways of doing things that had served the choir of St Basil's so well in previous years.

So angry was I that I did not wait for Tripplehorn to tell me whether he agreed with her or not. I marched out of the vestry, somehow found it in me to ask Tristan to bring the collection on Sunday evening, and left.

Fortunately Katie, who was staying with me this evening, managed to pick me up off the ground and told me that as far as she was concerned, if anybody deserved to be the subject of a complaint it was Hazel Ledworthy herself. Tripplehorn rang shortly afterwards. He was full of apologies for having had to bring the complaint to my attention, telling me that he thought the criticism was wholly unjustified and he would tell Hazel so himself, that I was doing a great job, and that as far as he was concerned Hazel was the worst advert for the choir and the greatest deterrent to any potential new recruits since the time that an infestation of woodlice had been found in Joan Trumpington's storage cupboard.

He went on to talk about Sunday's Harvest service, and the decision to use the service and the supper as a means of reaching out to the local community in place of the traditional entertainment. "I don't always agree with the PCC's decisions, as you know, but I think they have this one spot on," he said.

"You mean, in terms of generating a more vibrant congregation with a larger nucleus of younger professionals who can bring their time and talents to bear to help us achieve our vestry fund target and assure the church of a solid and workable future in years to come?" I suggested.

"Well, that too, of course," said Tripplehorn. "And the fact that after the supper I won't have to sit listening to the Load Of Old Cobblers using the music of Blow's *Salvator Mundi* to declaim the list of ingredients of a standard tin of Heinz spaghetti hoops."

Sunday 28th September

Traditionally on the Sunday of the Harvest service and supper, the choir always have the morning service off. I decided to go along anyway, for want of anything better to do. I was glad I did, because I found quite by chance that the printed copies of Arthur Ramsbottom's book will be available on Wednesday. They're being hand-delivered to the vicarage about midday. I was relieved to hear that the PCC have agreed to pay the printers' bill as soon as I get the invoice. I was less gratified to learn that somehow I've ended up having to take responsibility not only for the publicity, but also for storage of the books until they can be sold, remaindered or pulped, whichever is applicable. I know what my money is on at the moment.

It was clear that the advertising for this evening's service and supper had been effective, since we had a bigger congregation for the Harvest service than for any act of worship this year, including Easter. Tripplehorn had been asked to keep the music simple. "I'm quite happy to oblige on this occasion," he told me as we robed before the service.

I told him, as diplomatically as I could, that his reaction surprised me as he was usually so keen to show off the choir's repertoire to a large congregation.

"Yes," he replied, "but not when you've got pews full of street urchins drowning us out every time we open our mouths." I somehow can't see him taking on leadership of the proposed St Basil's Tiddler Club.

Usually for our services car parking is no problem – the complaints being usually about shortage of space for Zimmer frames and motorised invalid carriages – but today car parking space was at a premium, and there were a number of rather harassed latecomers including Tristan Chanctonbury, who made it, sweating and breathless, into the stalls just as we were finishing inviting the congregation to "Come Ye Thankful People Come."

He told me he hadn't been planning to stay for the supper but agreed with me that he deserved a stiff drink afterwards having run the three quarters of a mile from the Dun Cow Road car park in a sprightly five and a half minutes. We accordingly agreed that he would show me the all-important manuscript over supper.

The PCC certainly had got their act together tonight. There was a huge buffet and bar laid out at one end of the church hall just in front of the stage, with chairs and little tables scattered round the body of the hall and, in a corner of the hall, a dedicated baby and toddler area with special food and lots of things for the very young to play with. Tristan and I were among the front-runners for the refreshments. While we waited for a young couple in front of us to help themselves to some very tasty looking egg and prawn on chunky white bread, Tristan reached inside the bag he was holding and withdrew firstly the precious collection of hymn tunes and secondly a rather tatty red-covered book. The collection of hymn tunes was quite magnificently presented, in a large colourful volume, with attractive pictures on the cover and throughout the body of the collection. Afraid of getting the cover greasy as I was helping myself to food and drink, and noticing Tristan busily helping himself to slices of turkey and ham, I placed the manuscript carefully on the stage behind the buffet table to consider after I'd eaten, before casting my eye briefly over the other volume Tristan had given me. This was an old hymn book that must have dated about a hundred years – that much was obvious by the fact that the dates of death of some of the writers born before 1850 were left blank – and which, intriguingly, had a pencil "grade" against many of the hymns using the Greek alphabet. John Stainer seemed unable to put a foot wrong, I noticed, scoring an Alpha or double Alpha every time. But poor old W.H. Monk, apart from one Beta Minus, ended up with wall-to-wall Gammas and at one point the indignity of a Gamma Minus. I was quite surprised not to see an angry note saying "Five hundred lines after prep tonight."

As Tristan finished piling comestibles on to his plate, he hastened to point out that he doubted the red book had any real monetary value at all, emphasizing that he had brought it for my amusement and saying I was welcome to keep it for a rainy day or a dull sermon. But so absorbed was I in it that I realised I had no food on my plate and there was now a significant build-up of people behind me in the queue. I quickly helped myself to a selection of appetising fare, then went in pursuit of Tristan and having eventually found his table and placed my food on to it, I hastened back to the stage to retrieve the precious manuscript. It wasn't where I thought I'd left it but before I had time to become concerned as to its whereabouts, Alison Sparkes hurried up to me and said "If you're looking for that big picture book with the songs in, it's been taken down the other end."

A sudden ghastly suspicion flashed into my mind. "What do you mean?" I asked her.

"For the crèche," said Alison. "If you remember, just after the practice on Friday I asked the choir for contributions of books and toys for the children's corner. We assumed that it was something one of you had brought."

I don't think I have ever covered the distance from one corner of the hall to the other so quickly, notwithstanding the not inconsiderable number of obstacles in my path. Despite picking up four faults on the oddly shaped carry cot, and being minded to refuse at Lorinda Gartside's wheelchair, I successfully cleared the final tray of canapés and seconds later was among the heaving mass of juveniles feasting on such nutritious fare as potato crisps, Club biscuits and fruit squash and mutilating or destroying as many items as the church in the interests of promoting the good of the wider community felt it could spare.

By the time I had tracked down the collection, or what was left of it, the damage had quite literally been done. I first noticed a surly-looking curly-haired infant, with large acreages of chocolate around her mouth and globules of ice cream smeared unappealingly round her neck, had taken possession of three pages and was furiously decorating them with assorted multi-coloured squiggles which while they might make the Tate Modern in a couple of centuries did not enhance the antique value of the pages themselves one iota. Then I perceived a dark-haired girl with a ponytail using one of the pages to mop up the overturned contents of a plastic carton of some beverage which might have been Ruth Hartnell's home-made iced tea, Savemart Extra Sugary And Additive Packed Orange Squash or church hall heating oil. And a further couple of pages had been ripped and were being made into paper darts and paper balls by the more dexterous visitors in readiness to commence World War Three amongst the forest of unconsumed chicken nuggets.

Desperately trying to tell myself that an old book of hymns could not be *that* valuable, I gathered up the unmolested parts of the collection, stumbling over further candidates for the Tiddler Club, pots of half-consumed individual jelly portions and toy cars that in their present condition would have struggled to pass the Camberwick Green Garage MOT test. I decided there was no point in concealing the truth from Tristan and told him exactly what had happened.

To my relief, Tristan could not have been nicer. "Don't worry," he said. "These things happen. Besides, there's always the chance that even if it hadn't been damaged, the amount you actually cleared for it would have been a lot less than what it was last valued at."

"So how much do you think we would have got for it?" I asked him. "A few hundred quid, possibly, if we were lucky?"

"About three and a half thousand," said Tristan.

OCTOBER

Wednesday 1ˢᵗ October

After a long and difficult play rehearsal last night – not that I was really able to object as I won't be required next week – I could have done with a nice leisurely evening in, but there I was at six thirty going round to the vicarage after work to collect the books and bring them home, together with a vast number of A5 size advertising fliers.

I can't deny that the book itself, with a very professionally produced cover, looks most attractive. I'm pleased with the title, *Make A Joyful Noise*: not massively witty, perhaps, but certainly better than Arthur's brilliantly imaginative suggestion, *A History Of The Choir Of St Basil* and rather more reverent than Matthew's, namely *Flies Up Your Cassock*. I rang Arthur Ramsbottom to tell him the books were in. He duly appeared about twenty minutes later, and having picked up half a dozen copies went straight on to the matter of the launch party. "The vicar's told me we can do it on the 19ᵗʰ directly after the service," he said. "We'll get all the congregation up to the hall and I'll do a signing session."

I pursed my lips. Recently there seem to have been a glut of post-service beanos of one kind or another, from Mr and Mrs Humphries' cocktail party to celebrate their 50ᵗʰ wedding anniversary to Eloise Armitage's knees-up in celebration of the appearance of her watercolour, *Flotsam At Dawn*, in the Winkle Street Art Gallery. I asked Arthur if he thought there might be merit in something a little different.

"Well, that's very much down to you and the PCC," he said. "If you feel that you can organise it, that's fine by me, but personally I'd be happy for you just to lay some light refreshments on on the 19ᵗʰ and leave it at that." I'm not quite sure even now how I've managed to lumber myself with this additional responsibility, but I have. Then again, judging by the reaction to the prospect of publication that I've been able to gauge from other choir and congregation members, I will probably get away with providing a half bottle of Savemart Hartlepool 1983 vintage elderberry and a single pack of economy cupcakes. Served in the church hall broom cupboard.

Friday 3ʳᵈ October

Well, Arthur can't say I'm shirking in my publicity for his book. Not only have I arranged for details of it to go on to the St Basil's website, but tonight I took a supply of copies to offer for sale to choir members at rehearsal ahead of official publication day in a fortnight's time. Whatever my views are about the standard of writing I have to try and be as positive as I can in selling copies bearing in mind the need for vestry fund money.

The reaction of members of the choir to my sales drive was perhaps predictable. Brian, Craig, Eileen and Ken bought copies immediately. Ruth said that as the new member the history would mean nothing to her, and that she would rather not buy one. Cora flicked through the copy I'd offered her and as soon as she saw her name and the glowing if hideously servile tributes to her generosity and dedication purchased three copies. Margaret said she'd love to buy one but money was a bit tight this month on account of her having to pay to replace her mother's overflow pipe and also fork out a sizeable sum for the privilege of the Highfield Road scrap dealers coming round to take delivery of Oscar, her sick Ford Fiesta, and have it put to sleep. I decided that as I'd left my asbestos suit at home I had better not approach Hazel Ledworthy, but I would have been wasting my time anyway, since I heard her curtly informing Arthur that she had not got her reading glasses with her. Silly of me to think she might have brought them to choir practice in the first place. Henry Peasgood turned disdainfully over a few pages of the copy I'd given him, grunted "It was October not September 1972 that the G below middle C stuck in the Venite" and handed it back. Irving Cattermole said he'd wait till it appeared in the charity shop and get one then if he found he had the requisite 10p to spare. Lesley said "I've got no money with me tonight, but I'll buy one on Sunday providing there's nothing rude about me in it." I decided not to tell her it was even worse than that. She isn't mentioned at all.

I expected Tripplehorn to buy at least two copies, but all he said was "I might get one on Sunday for my friend Max. It could be just what he needs with his condition."

"What condition's that?" I enquired.

"He suffers from chronic insomnia," said Tripplehorn.

I can think of a few things I wouldn't mind sticking in his Venite.

Sunday 5th October

Although we have agreed that we will only begin to offer copies to the congregation at the launch party on the 19th, which we have nominated as the official publication date, we decided to offer flyers at this morning's service in anticipation of advance orders and also to generate interest in the launch party itself. Arthur was all for leaving flyers on all the seats but the vicar vetoed the idea. I can understand that, I have to say. If every single organiser of activities within the church community, from the St Chad's Homeless Hostel House To House Collection Coordinator to the Secretary Of The West Shires Christian Under 40's Single Parent Fellowship And Welfare Cooperative, put flyers out on the seats to promote their various activities, there'd be no room to sit down. The vicar agreed a compromise, namely that an announcement would be made during the notices at the end of the service, and flyers could be distributed to members of the congregation as they left afterwards. How I found myself processing with the choir into and out of church clutching not only my folder of music but the entire supply of flyers for distribution afterwards I'm not entirely certain. Nor can I quite work out how, during the recessional hymn, the pile of them parted company from the rest of the material I was holding as I rounded the corner into the home straight. I suppose some good did come out of it. By the time Lesley had pricked three of them with the heel of her left ankle boot, Craig had left the imprint of his size eight brogues on a further two, and Matthew had transferred a generous portion of chewing gum from his right trainer to another one, we had five less to get rid of. Leaving us with a paltry 395.

Margaret had a suggestion to make after the service. "You should try getting the books into some church bookshops," she said. "A lot of their customers would enjoy a book about a local church choir. There's a good Christian bookstore in town. The Books For Eternity Shop in Market Lane. Why don't you see if they'll take some flyers and copies when the time comes? And if that's no good, there's the New Life Bookshop."

"What, in town?" I asked her.

"No, it's about twenty five miles away," she replied. "It's a lovely shop though. Been owned and run by the same man for the last sixty years. Obviously he's not as sprightly as he was, and his hearing and sight are going a bit. But his heart's in the right place."

I'm glad to hear it. I only hope the rest of him is.

Even in spite of the best combined efforts of Lesley, Craig and Matthew, and a concerted distribution drive afterwards, we had a huge number of flyers left after church this morning. In sheer desperation, Arthur suggested that each member of the choir who had not by that stage made good their escape might take home a supply. "To send out to all deserving relatives, acquaintances and friends," he suggested.

I'm sure that it was out of politeness, rather than any real conviction that there would be any more than the most derisory take-up, which caused us to grab a handful each. Frankly, I'm not sure any one of my friends actually deserves to have their ears bent or their conscience pricked by the offer of such unappealing merchandise – other than those who have gone out of their way to upset me. I suppose I have a few who fall into that category. My Auntie Edwina whose pet ferret Gentle extracted a large chunk out of my leg on Boxing Day 1974. My plumber who succeeded in fitting an entire shower unit on the wrong end of my bath. And Angus McPetrie, who ruined my chances of winning the Henderson Prize at my Year 11 school sports day by tying my shoelaces together at the start of the egg and spoon race.

Tuesday 7ᵗʰ October

Went along to Books For Eternity, which I did recall having visited once before, at lunchtime. It was only when I walked in that I found that since my last visit it had turned into a teddy bear shop.

Decided that I might as well try the New Life Bookshop. Fearful that I might waste a couple of gallons of petrol by driving there to find that it had become a pizza restaurant or an Indian takeaway, I thought it best to telephone ahead. Relieved at any rate to be informed by the elderly-sounding man who answered the telephone that he was still selling Christian books, I told him about our volume and asked if he would be prepared to sell it.

"Sounds very promising," he said. "I take it they come with envelopes?"

I hastened to make it clear to him that I was trying to promote a book, not a packet of Christmas cards, and told him for the second time what it was about. Fortunately he said he'd be happy to take a dozen on a sale or return basis.

"I'll come round with them next Friday, just before publication, if that's okay," I said to him.

"That would be fine," he said, "only if you're going to write the prices on the back, please can you do it in pencil so that we can rub them out when we're selling them. We keep having to take our normal card suppliers to task for that."

Having once again informed him what I was actually going to be delivering to him, and gone for the third time into considerable detail about the book's content, I told him I'd see him next week.

"Just one other thing," he said. "Is the illustration the same on each card?"

I give up.

Friday 10ᵗʰ October

At choir tonight, Alison, Zoe and Matthew formally announced the Word Games evening two weeks on Saturday. It's open to all choir members and their friends and families, with admission absolutely free but participants being asked to contribute to a retiring collection. It's clear that they have a pretty ambitious and comprehensive programme, and as they're taking responsibility for the whole shooting match, with my having no part in the organisation, I'm really quite looking forward to it. It will include such radio gems as *My Word, Many A Slip* and *Just A Minute* but also TV favourites such as *Give Us A Clue* and *Call My Bluff.* I gather that there will not be a fish or chip in sight and that refreshments will consist of squash and biscuits. Served, I hope, in paper cups. The last thing the police will want on a busy Saturday night in town is wine glasses and mugs being hurled across the village hall following Cora

Willoughby-Smith's failed attempts to mime *How To Succeed In Business Without Really Trying.*

"I don't know one called *My Word*," said Lesley, as she helped Tripplehorn distribute copies of Edgar Bainton's *And I Saw A New Heaven.*

"Oh, you must do," said Rachel. "If you remember, they gave them a well known phrase or quotation and they had to tell a story with a punchline consisting of a play on that phrase or quotation – you know, 'You can't have your cake and eat it' becoming 'You can't have your kayak and heat it.'"

We spent a long time on the Bainton, which we were to be performing on Sunday, and I could see Tripplehorn losing patience with the basses. Henry Peasgood in particular seemed to be in a world of his own. It was only as the copies were being gathered up again afterwards that his eyes lit up and he seemed to return to normality. "I've got it," he said. "Anne, Di, thaw at Newhaven."

"I beg your pardon?" said Tripplehorn.

"Two girls, crossing the Channel from Dieppe during a snowstorm. They're sitting in the bowels of the ship, getting colder and colder, and their father tries to cheer them up by telling them 'Anne, Di, thaw at Newhaven.' As in 'And I Saw A New Heaven.'"

"And it's taken you the last thirty five minutes to work that out?" said Tripplehorn.

"About that," grinned Henry Peasgood.

"I'd stick to heating kayaks if I were you," said Tripplehorn.

Sunday 12th October

Tickets for the play and carol concert went on sale at church this morning. Ruth thrust twenty tickets at me, ten for each night, and said to me "I expect you to get rid of all these by the end of this month." I'm sure I'll have no difficulty in getting rid of them. Actually asking for people to part with hard-earned cash and leave the comfort of their firesides for the supreme privilege of watching a lesson in the Art Of Coarse Acting is a different matter altogether.

Of course, it was fatal for Tripplehorn to come in to the vestry at the start of the service and say to us "Any mention of blizzard-bound cross Channel ferries and I shan't be responsible for the consequences." I'd rather forgotten Henry's dismal Friday attempt to follow in the footsteps of Frank Muir and Dennis Norden, but with the title page of Bainton's immortal anthem staring me in the face throughout a desperately drab sermon, I couldn't resist seeing if I could do any better. I was quite pleased with my Chinese pub landlord who preferred parquet flooring – On Wood Chris Chan Sold Jars – but the call to a lady firefighter to water down a West London grocery display – Hose, Anna, In Eggs(Chelsea's) – or the assurance to the TV chat show host that Ollie's friend is giving financial support to a rabbi – Stan Foots Jew Bill, Harty – is definitely work in progress.

Tuesday 14th October

On arrival home from work, I was surprised to receive a telephone call from a Reginald Cheesewright, advising me that following a reshuffle in the editorial department of the local paper he has just taken over as their chief reporter. He told me he'd heard that I was the "publicity guru" for the church choir history, and he'd also gathered that I'd managed to get some copies of the book into the New Life Bookshop. When I confirmed that I was planning to go over there on Friday, he asked me if I'd be prepared to meet up with him in a couple of weeks so he could do a feature on the book and on the choir. Following a call to Tripplehorn, it was confirmed that Cheesewright will attend choir practice on Friday week. He will interview Arthur about the book and will also sit in on part of the practice itself, with a view to completing the necessary research.

But although that was encouraging as far as the vestry fund was concerned, I felt frankly discouraged by what was a pretty dire play rehearsal again tonight. At least we managed to do a full run-through and there were some sections, chiefly early on, where we did quite passably without books. Ruth said, I am sure to encourage us, "You're further on than St Stephen's Drama Group were last December with *P'tang Yang Kipper Bang* with a month and a half to go."

At coffee I mentioned to Ken that I'd never heard of the St Stephen's Drama Group.

"Probably not surprising," he said, "since the producer emigrated to Botswana just before Christmas."

Ruth mentioned to me something that hadn't previously occurred to me, namely that under copyright law I am obliged to deposit half a dozen copies of Arthur's book with various libraries including the British Library and the Bodleian Library. I'm sure that the legislation was not intended to cover books of such limited appeal or such doubtful literary quality, but there it is. If I must, I must. It'll be six less opportunities to make more money for the vestry. On the other hand, I must say I love the thought of gowned boffins and Oxford dons sitting grouped in musty libraries three or four centuries from now, emitting chuckles of academic delight at how Mildred Fossett upset the stallholders at the November 1981 choir jumble sale by providing full cream milk for the refreshment table instead of semi-skimmed.

I must bear *P'tang Yang Kipper Bang* in mind for Saturday week. I'd like to see Cora Willoughby-Smith trying to mime that.

Friday 17th October

Katie had booked us seats at the theatre tonight in Salisbury so I asked to be excused choir. As luck would have it, the New Life Bookshop wasn't far off the route, so rather than make an extra journey we decided to leave in the middle of the afternoon intending to call at the bookshop with Arthur's books and then to go on for a meal before the play.

We arrived at the New Life Bookshop in good time, with twelve copies of Arthur's book for them to stock on a sale or return basis. Following the absurd dialogue I had had with the owner ten days ago, I decided that the direct businesslike approach would be the best, and accordingly walked purposefully up to the rather frail-looking old man who was sitting by the till and said "Right. Here we are. Twelve copies of *Make A Joyful Noise*, sale or return, plus a confirmatory delivery note and supply of flyers. I'll put them on the main table display. I'm seeing the local paper next week so you should start to get some enquiries shortly. Thank you very much for your assistance."

I was about to place the copies on the table and walk smartly out of the shop but before I could do so the man looked round at the door behind him and said "I think it's the owner you need to speak to, not me."

"So you've no authority to accept the books on his behalf?" I asked him.

"Oh, no," he replied. "I don't work here. I'm just a customer."

At that moment, an even more doddery-looking individual appeared through the back door. "Did somebody want me?" he enquired.

Having ascertained that this new arrival was in fact the shop owner, I took a deep breath and launched into my speech again. Indicating with my left hand the dozen copies in my right hand, I said "Here they are. As promised on the phone last week. Twelve copies of *Make A Joyful Noise*, and some flyers. I'll just….."

"Just a minute," the owner interrupted. "Can I take a look at them please."

"Of course," I said.

I handed them to the owner who studied carefully the material on the back of the top book, then did a careful count of the books and scribbled some figures on to a piece of paper in front of him before looking up at me again. "Yes, that's all perfectly in order," he said. "Very good. That'll be £84, please. Would you like them in a bag?"

Sunday 19th October

Launch party and signing for Arthur's book.

As I walked down the church path this morning, an elderly lady in a flowing green dress and a hat full of plastic fruit and vegetables marched up beside me, and announced herself. "I'm Prunella Swineshead-

Havergal," she informed me. "I've seen from the St Basil's website that the signing of a choir history is to be taking place today and I'm determined to be at the front of the queue for it." Though she is now living in a remote community near Hereford by the name of Michaelchurch Escley, she told me that she used to be a regular worshipper at St Basil's and described herself as the "choir's sometime number 1 fan and chief groupie." The mind boggles.

It was announced during the service that the signing, with accompanying eats, would take place at the church hall afterwards. The lure of marmite sandwiches, miniature pork pies and chocolate Swiss Roll to go with the coffee and tea proved irresistible to a goodly percentage of the congregation. Unfortunately, so absorbed were they in this veritable feast that they seemed to forget all about the signing itself. The result was that Arthur the author, who should have been the principal centre of attention, was left sitting alone at his signing table with little more self-confidence and optimism than a farmful of turkeys on hearing the first Christmas carols of the winter.

Feeling rather sorry for him, I prised Prunella Swineshead-Havergal from the pork pie plate and steered her diplomatically towards Arthur at the signing table. Immediately, and much to my relief, his eyes lit up; he sprang to his feet, threw his arms round her and kissed her on both cheeks. It was clear that he had been on very friendly terms with her all the time she had been at St Basil's, and this reunion was clearly the best news he had had all morning. Within seconds they were seated together at the signing table exchanging reminiscences of times past. By now, some other would-be customers were taking their place in the queue behind Prunella, but so engrossed was the author with his first potential purchaser that I doubt if he would have noticed if a herd of buffalo had invaded the village hall and begun mixing themselves up with Mrs Merridew's marmite soldiers. When it became obvious that Arthur was not only busy soaking up the praise for the book he was signing but also gathering copious material for volumes two, three and four, those towards the back of the queue decided enough was enough and started heading for the door. Far from registering concern, however, Arthur merely requested Joan Trumpington, who was hovering nearby, to go and fetch two mugs of coffee and a couple of pieces of Swiss Roll, saying it was "the least we can do to honour the presence of such a worthy guest." In due course the aforementioned refreshment arrived and Joan set it down on the table. Unfortunately Arthur chose that moment to launch into a "sneak preview" of the incident on page 61 involving the 1950's contralto Madeline Aberhosan and the jar of mouldy chutney she'd entered for the produce competition at the church fete, choosing to illustrate her extravagant reaction to failing to clinch equal third prize with Brigadier Sir Algernon

Chievely by a sweep of the hand. A sweep which, unfortunately, made contact with the edge of the table. The result was dramatic. The table, a small collapsible one and not the sturdiest of constructions, was catapulted into the air, and as a result the cups, plates, saucers and the contents thereof were all sent flying as well. It was Ambrose Bassett, third in the queue, who was called upon to revisit his schoolboy soccer skills by deflecting a lump of chocolate sponge with his head, whilst Gordon Banks himself would have been proud of the dive executed by Portia Rumbleton, next in the queue, to fend off a shower of cheap charity-shop china. The table, meanwhile, had fallen victim to the coffee-covered floor and having executed a couple of graceful Lionel Blairesque turns, was last seen slithering off in a south-westerly direction, rumoured to be bound for Cape Finisterre.

Fortunately none of the copies of the book had been soiled or damaged. Moreover, Prunella Swineshead-Havergal was happy to wait until the area immediately about Arthur Ramsbottom had ceased to be deemed a danger zone before resuming her conversation with him as though nothing had happened and going away with no less than five paid-for copies. But by the time she had left, all the other prospective buyers had been frightened off, and the only ones left in the hall were the stalwart band of helpers finishing the task of gathering pieces of broken china and sweeping up the sad remains of the plucky but vanquished marmite soldiers. And who I rather fear regarded the procurement of a signed choir history as lower on their immediate wish list than deflea-ing the church hall gents' loobrush.

I blame the Internet myself.

Tuesday 21st October

With a take-up from the advertising flyer I'd sent regarding the choir history hovering around the nought per cent mark, it was quite a relief to be able to take my mind off it with a play rehearsal tonight. Cora was off with a bad back, and we actually enjoyed one of our better rehearsals, with none of her prima-donna-ish antics and a very congenial coffee break with Ruth's delicious home-made cakes.

As we sat drinking our coffee, discussion drifted round to Saturday's word games evening. Matthew Sparkes was very clued up about the whole thing. "We're going to start with *Call My Bluff,*" he said, "then go on to *Give Us A Clue*, a sort of shortened version of *Weakest Link*, and then *Countdown*."

"That sounds a fairly comprehensive programme," Ruth remarked.

"Oh, that's only the first half," said Matthew. "Then after coffee we've got *My Word, Just A Minute,* and as a grand finale, something based on *I'm Sorry I Haven't A Clue*."

"Well all I can say is, it's just as well the clocks are going back this weekend," said Ruth with feeling.

It does rather amuse me, the way she's so disparaging about fundraising events into which she's had no input. Only the other day, she told me "in strict confidence" that if given the choice between selling Arthur's book to the congregation and selling live crocodiles to handbag manufacturers, she'd be catching the first plane to the banks of the river Nile. Then again, as far as Saturday is concerned, perhaps she's got a point. I can see the whole thing lasting well into the small hours. I suppose if it does threaten to overrun, they could combine a few of the later rounds. And Ruth, who raised the issue in the first place, could volunteer to don one of Frank Muir's famous pink bow ties and act out one of the more obscure words from the *Oxford English Dictionary* before uttering, without hesitation, deviation or repetition, a contemptuous Anne Robinson-esque farewell on the down platform at Mornington Crescent.

Friday 24th October

Reginald Cheesewright duly attended tonight's choir practice. He announced he would spend the first 45 minutes observing our rehearsal and would then go into the vestry for an interview with Arthur about the book.

However, for all the notes he made during the first half of the evening, I'm not sure he will have come away with a hugely accurate picture of the choir and its personalities. Hazel Ledworthy did not give her usual scowl as the music was distributed – then again we have done *God So Loved The World* about 582 times so she probably knows most of it by now – and Matthew Sparkes' opportunity to disrupt proceedings was all but eliminated by the confiscation of his comic paper complete with free "Soak Your Friends" water pistol. Craig Dumbleton was away so there was no way of knowing who had presented their apologies for absence from the Shoeburyness And District Light Railway Collectors' Club half-yearly general meeting. And Tripplehorn, having sensibly provided some safe pieces with which to impress our guest, did not once feel the need to tell us how he had heard sweeter sounds from his pet cockatoo on being treated to a fast spin dry in his Hotpoint.

At eight fifteen our guest went off with Arthur and it wasn't till nine twenty, as I was disposing of the paper drinks cups, that he reappeared, alone, from the vestry and asked for a strong black coffee.

"How are you getting on?" I asked him.

"If I tell you," Reginald replied wearily, "that he's just been telling me the story of how the vicar announced the Benedicite instead of the Benedictus during one matins, I think you'll get the picture."

I certainly did. That story was on page four. Of one hundred and seventy six.

Saturday 25th October

Since Matthew Sparkes, who insisted on dealing with the lion's share of the organisation of the word games evening we have just had, was on a fairly steep learning curve, it may help to make a note of those areas which he will wish to look at should he ever decide he can bring himself to organise a repeat performance. Preferably not before about 2050.

Number one – the fact that you have seen a video of Lionel Blair, one of the *Give Us A Clue* veterans, failing to successfully mime *Amityville 2: The Possession* is perhaps not a good reason to force an identical task on to Henry Peasgood, who has as much miming aptitude as a one-legged carthorse and as much ability to take some good-humoured ribbing as a Prussian car park attendant.

Number two – it is probably a good idea, when preparing the *Call My Bluff* round, to avoid words of which over half those present in the hall know the definition, and to include the true definition amongst the three given, especially when those endeavouring to divine the correct answer include Ruth Hartnell's next-door neighbour who happens to be a contributor to the latest edition of the *Concise Oxford Dictionary*.

Number three – when playing *Just A Minute*, it is important to ensure firstly that any implement used for the registering of a challenge actually works, secondly that the referee has a watch with a functioning second hand, and thirdly that the contestants are made aware that deviation from the subject is a challengeable offence, thus preventing future generations of Arthur Ramsbottoms copying what the present one did and when bidden to speak for sixty seconds on the subject of the petrol engine instead chose to chunter on for three and a half minutes on the defective lighting system on the Lamb And Flag roundabout at the top end of Gaslight Road.

Number four – if with the commendable aim of saving money on the outlay for the raffle you undertake a purge on your family's store of cheap wines and cordials with a view to offering them as prizes, ensure that labels stating their true age and value are discreetly removed first, particularly those marked with prices in pounds shillings and pence and an advice that they are best opened before the 1st March 1968.

Number five – if endeavouring to imitate Anne Robinson's acerbic appraisals of her contestants' performances in *The Weakest Link*, it is as well to equip oneself with a stock of well-chosen expressions of disparagement that actually make sense rather than asking at the end of every round which of the group is one sandwich short of a pop-up toaster.

Finally – if a decision is taken to hold a retiring collection rather than charge admission, on the basis of a comment made at a recent PCC meeting by the retired solicitor Clarence Fitzherbert that there may be copyright infringements by charging to perform games that are performed on television and radio, it is perhaps best to ensure that the person with the begging bowl is not allowed to stand by the sink gossiping with the washer-uppers about the failure of Mrs Bletherington to be elected as deputy chairman of the Women's Institute Jams And Preserve Making Steering Committee, only arriving at the door after two thirds of the punters have left. And also to ensure that the lady likely to be among the most generous of the donors, if not THE most generous of all, is not awarded a Little Chef freebie lollipop as the booby prize for the most inept performance of the evening, regardless of the quality of her attempt in the *Give Us A Clue* round to act out *Why Don't You Switch Off Your Television Set And Go And Do Something Less Boring Instead.*

Sunday 26th October

It was the start of half-term week today. Inevitably this meant a depleted choir and a rather dull music list, and I arrived at church with no real sense of anticipation or enthusiasm. As I robed, I was already thinking ahead to what I'd got planned for the afternoon. Then, in walked Jane Markwick. Dressed in tight denim, she looked absolutely unbelievable. She marched straight up to me, gave me a huge kiss on the lips and said "How are we today, then, gorgeous?"

It got better. Over coffee afterwards, she told me that the novelty of denture cleansing, pipe and slippers fetching and remembering to collect *Yours* magazine on her way home from lectures, had worn off and she had leapt over the bath chair, slid down the stairlift rail and walked out of Cyril's life for good. She asked me how the play was going, and I told her I would be enjoying it a hundred times more and would also be a good deal more willing to promote it to potential vestry fund contributors if she was able to be there for a rehearsal or two. "Why don't we rehearse tonight?" she said. "Tell me where it is, and I'll be there. You can take me for a drink afterwards."

Despite getting on my mobile to the other players immediately, I had a rather mixed response. Ruth was free and happy to host, Arthur was also available, and Cora said she'd be able to get there late. But Matthew had gone away with his parents for half-term, Rachel had some urgent work she needed to finish before Monday morning, and Ken had arranged to go out for dinner. Nonetheless, we were at least a quorum, and so we fixed it up for seven thirty.

I'm ashamed to say that despite enjoying a lovely afternoon walk with Katie, I couldn't stop thinking about Jane and the prospect of rehearsing with her this evening. Somehow I got through the afternoon without making Katie suspect my mind was anywhere but on her, then, tense with expectancy, drove round to Ruth's. Only to be told, on arrival, that Lesley had just rung to say Jane couldn't make it after all.

"Did she say why?" I asked.

"Yes," said Ruth. "She's had to go out with Ainslie tonight."

To be honest, I can't say I was entirely shocked or surprised. Or really cared. Provided she's content with whoever she chooses in life, I shouldn't worry if she throws in her lot with the president-elect of the Cayman Islands or captain of the Ballybunion ice hockey team. Or both, for that matter.

After some discussion we agreed there'd be nothing to lose by going through some of the play tonight, but I just couldn't wait for the rehearsal to finish. I staggered home at nine, more disillusioned and unenthusiastic over this play, and less inclined to sell tickets for it, than I think I ever have been. Rang Lesley to ask if Jane would be available on Tuesday night when our next rehearsal was due to take place but was told Jane was going away tomorrow and would be unlikely to be home again for several more weeks.

"By the way," I said. "Who is Ainslie?"

"He's an old English sheepdog," said Lesley.

As I say, as long as she's happy with him.

Tuesday 28th October

A difficult play rehearsal tonight. Moreover, early reports of ticket sales for the play not good. Whilst I can understand Margaret's mother complaining that she and her family always get very bad coughs and sneezes round the beginning of December, it strikes me as being more than a little coincidental that virtually every friend and acquaintance of Rachel has arranged to fly to Miami Beach for a poolside wedding celebration on the day of the play's opening performance, and Matthew's suggestion that all his friends will be too worn out to attend following his school's annual traditional welly-wanging contest the day before stretched credibility, not to mention Ruth's patience, to the limit.

"What about you, Arthur?" Ruth enquired as she poured out the coffee. "Can't you persuade a few of your friends from the Senior Citizens Club to come along? Your friend Moira for instance."

"I fear she's still in shock from that gun-shooting incident," said Arthur. "It's quite traumatised her."

Somewhat concerned, I followed Ruth out to the kitchen to help her bring in the cakes and the home-made biscuits. "That's a bit worrying about Moira, isn't it?" I said. "I feel rather bad we've mentioned it now."

"I wouldn't do," said Ruth. "Seeing as the gunshot in question was actually on stage. In our production of *Puss In Boots*. In 1978."

Friday 31ˢᵗ October

No Margaret at choir this evening, as she was helping to organise the Alternative Halloween Party in the scout hut. Not that that prevented our choir practice being interrupted by a group of teenagers bursting in with pots of paint, and following our refusal to acknowledge their less than polite requests for some form of refreshment or monetary donation, daubed the back row of seats in interesting shades of green, purple and shocking pink.

Margaret would have been sorry to have missed the practice. Not because of the newspaper article by Reginald Cheesewright that was passed around tonight; although it acknowledged the importance of the choir's contribution to church life, it was pretty uncomplimentary about Arthur's book and frankly unenthusiastic about the signing session Arthur has organised for next Tuesday at the New Life Bookshop. We were, however, practising a couple of Margaret's favourite choruses, specially requested by the couple at whose wedding we are singing on 22ⁿᵈ November with the choir fees going to the vestry fund. There's another wedding on 2ⁿᵈ January and we agreed that if we haven't quite hit the target we might come to a similar arrangement for that one, too.

"Presumably they're the ones who had the banns read for the first time last Sunday," said Eileen. "I think they were in church."

"Oh, yes, them," Lesley said with a giggle. "They did look rather anxious when the vicar asked if there were any objections."

"It was on the tip of my tongue to object, actually," said Tripplehorn. Suddenly his face turned quite grave. "In fact if it wasn't for the vestry fund money we need, I almost certainly would have done."

"If it's the couple I think it is, I'm not that surprised," said Lesley. "Was it the rumour that he's got criminal convictions for gross indecency and has ten grand outstanding in child maintenance from two earlier relationships and she's believed to be wanted by the police for taking part in three earlier bigamous marriages and arranging fake marriage ceremonies for fifteen illegal Iranian immigrants?"

"Oh, nothing like that," said Tripplehorn. "They want us to sing *I Only Have Eyes For You* during the signing of the register. If that isn't a ground for objection I don't know what is."

Sunday 2nd November

Did not get up in the brightest of spirits this morning, with the prospect of a long sing at church, two hours' set painting and then a three hour rehearsal booked in for this afternoon in the church hall. Tripplehorn had a lovely combination of All Saints Day and All Souls Day music lined up, including Stanford's delicious *Justorum Animae*, but sadly I wasn't in the right frame of mind to enjoy it today.

Because the service finished rather late, I decided to go straight to the hall to make a start on the set painting. For some reason the paints had been placed right at the top of the cupboard which Ruth had requisitioned for the use of the drama group. Nonetheless, I had every confidence that I could reach the pot of white paint nearest the front – confidence which was found to be sadly misplaced when, as I endeavoured to manoeuvre it away from its position, it suddenly toppled over and the entire contents cascaded down on to my head.

Managed to retain sufficient presence of mind to suggest to Arthur, who had wandered in a couple of minutes previously, that a step ladder or some suitable alternative implement might be found to assist those wanting to remove further items from the top of the cupboard, then went off home to see how easily the paint would wash off. Fifteen rinses of my hair later, I was beginning to get some idea. Still, it did at least give me a reasonable pretext to escape further set-painting responsibilities and the chance to enjoy a relaxed lunch at home, and I was actually feeling more positive as I set out for the church hall again in a new set of clothing. Complete with a woolly balaclava.

Ruth called us all together into the middle of the hall for a pre-rehearsal pep-talk. "It's always an exciting moment," she announced, "when for the first time we find ourselves rehearsing on the same piece of ground that we're going to be performing on. At last you'll start to appreciate the dimensions within which we are working, and you can start to think of an audience down below you providing some feedback on your performances. So we're going to run the entire show using the stage this afternoon. I am looking forward to it tremendously. Act 1 beginners please."

With such a stirring speech of encouragement, it seemed that nobody could fail to feel an upsurge of confidence and optimism, and it was with this positive spirit in mind that Ruth climbed on to the stage, walked towards stage left, suddenly lost her footing, and disappeared spectactularly into the abyss below.

At that precise moment, the bad-tempered hall caretaker, Mr Pockett, appeared from the broom cupboard and demanded "Which prize idiot has gone and removed those wooden boards from the stage?"

"I did," Arthur Ramsbottom confessed. "We needed something to stand on so we could reach the paints."

"Congratulations," said Pockett. "Those boards were covering a huge hole in the stage flooring. It's a death trap as it stands now. Just make sure nobody walks across it till I've had the chance to do something about it."

You have to give the man ten out of his ten for his health and safety concerns, though nought out of ten for his timing. And slightly less than nought out of ten for his skills when it came to hoisting the generously built Ruth Hartnell, rendered even podgier by what sounded like an excessive Sunday lunch she had just consumed, from the grimly enormous accumulation of waste, rubble and other detritus in the area immediately underneath the stage flooring. It didn't help, I suppose, that Ruth for all her organisational aptitude had the litheness and agility of a Scunthorpe Borough Council sewage transporter, and the patience and understanding of a charging rhinoceros. And while it was fascinating from a church hall historian's point of view to discover the diversity of relics from the church hall's stage's architectural and indeed archaeological past, there was little aesthetic pleasure to be gained from the combined rescue operation that followed. I suppose the balaclava, which by the end was caked with dust and soot, was due for the British Heart Foundation 20p bargain box anyway. Less ecstatic about the fate of my newly-laundered jumper.

By the time we had regrouped, enthusiasm for continuing the rehearsal was not exactly red hot. For one thing, we were now temporarily without our director, Ruth having been transported off to A & E by Rachel as a precaution. For another, Pockett had announced that the scar in the middle of the stage had been widened so much by Ruth's unscheduled journey into its nether regions that it would be quite impossible to use the stage again until major repairs had been undertaken, and he did not foresee that happening this side of Christmas.

"Of course, there is another worry," said Cora as we trooped disconsolately from the hall. "If Ruth has sustained any lasting injury, she may not be able to do her part in the play. And I really can't think of anyone else who could step in."

"Before Rachel left, she did mention a couple of ladies at church who belong to the town dramatic society," I said. "They might be worth asking."

"Who's that?" Cora enquired.

"Elspeth Dewberry and Florence Muxworth," I replied.

"I think not," said Cora briskly. "Elspeth has all the thespian skills of a plate of tapioca. And Ruth has never forgiven Florence for upstaging her during her denouement speech in her 1992 St Bartholomew's Players production of *Mr Macaroni And The Exploding Pizza Pie*."

Tuesday 4th November

Got a phone call from Arthur Ramsbottom first thing. He told me that his car was on the blink and he would therefore have difficulty in getting to his signing session at the New Life Bookshop, but said that as he was sure I was going wasn't I, could I please give him a lift. I'd actually hoped I could avoid having to attend, especially as I had a mountain of work on my desk, but had no choice but to agree to go over and work late tonight instead. Tuesday night is rehearsal night, but play rehearsals are now temporarily on hold, at least until Ruth has made a decision on her future involvement in the light of her accident. Having said that, I think I'd have preferred a full evening's line-bashing to a long and tedious lunchtime car journey, sitting in turn behind a horse box, a tractor and a manure transporter, listening to Arthur prattling on about the signing session and the arrangements for it. As we came into the town and drove up the High Street, I couldn't resist rather naughtily saying to him "I hope the police have remembered to cone off the area round the shop so that the queuing purchasers don't obstruct the pavement."

To my amazement, he looked anxiously towards me and said to me "Can I possibly leave it to you to check with them that they will?"

I don't know whether I felt sorrier for him or for me.

The owner of the shop was all smiles when we arrived. "Splendid, splendid," he said, beaming at us through his horn-rimmed spectacles. "How very good of you to come. I've been looking forward to seeing you all morning and we're so glad you could be here." I exchanged confident glances with Arthur as we transported two piles of books towards the middle of the shop. "That's right," the owner twittered on. "If you go straight through that far door you'll find it's the handbasin in the first room on the right that needs the new washer."

It was well past the time the hordes of queuing customers were due to be admitted for the first precious autographed copies when we finally got the owner to understand why exactly Arthur Ramsbottom was here. Although to be fair to the owner, who kindly went out of his way to make Arthur a very generously-sugared coffee – I watched as all six cubes slithered out of the packet – and myself a cup of oxtail soup smothered in semi-skimmed milk, he would probably have done himself and his premises more good had he asked Arthur to stick to plumbing duties and ignore the stampede of members of the public into his shop over the ensuing hour. All four of them. The first displayed a keen interest in Arthur's book. For a good ten minutes he flicked through the pages, occasionally smiling, sometimes even permitting himself a chuckle. He stroked the stubble on his chin, and then proceeded to ask us a number of probing questions, recording all the answers in a notebook. How long had he been a writer? Was this his first book? What gave him the idea to write it? Who provided him with the information? How many copies were printed? How many had been sold? How else was it being promoted? And Arthur, of course, loved every second of it, answering the questions with an enthusiasm that a half-starved cat might accord to a saucerful of clotted Devon cream, while I chipped in with additional information as necessary. "Very interesting," the man mused as he put his notebook away. "I think this could be very interesting indeed." And off he went, without buying a single copy.

And there was no joy from the other three customers. The second customer was a representative from the Adventist Press anxious for a further order for a book proclaiming the end of the world was taking place on 1st December and urging retailers to get customers to buy their copies to beat the Christmas rush. The third, an elderly lady in a thick fawn raincoat, spent a good half hour thumbing tearfully through the pages of one of the newer Bible translations, as if desperate for divine enlightenment and solace in a time of grief, only to slam the book down in disgust and proclaim to us that her research had not brought her anywhere nearer to solving 2 Across in the *Sun* Quick Crossword. And the fourth went away puzzled, having asked the shop owner for a copy of the *Spiritual Exercises Of Ignatius Loyola* and being referred to the aerobics equipment store at the bottom of Juxon Street.

As we were leaving, I mischievously turned to the owner and said "I'll be back next week to fix the leaky radiator in the stock room."

"Oh, thank you," the owner replied. "How much do I owe you for the sandwiches?"

Friday 7th November

Arrived at choir a little late, as I'd agreed to accompany Katie to her final confirmation class before the confirmation service itself which takes place on Advent Sunday 30th. However I did get to the church in time to hear Tripplehorn announce that Ruth's injuries have turned out to be worse than first believed, and she will be in plaster for at least six weeks. But whilst it seems that she will be unable to appear on stage in the play, she is apparently very anxious for the show to go on and has asked us round to her house on Sunday afternoon so we can discuss how we can continue in the absence of both a cast member and a venue. Poor Ruth must be in a bad way. I didn't think the word "discuss" existed in her lexicon.

"If you ask me," sniffed Hazel Ledworthy, "I think it's absurd carrying on with the show at all. Surely we can simply do an extended concert."

"If we do, we'll lose a lot of potential audience members," said Ken Foulkes. "When there's a will there's a way. I mean, look at Marissa Anstruther who insisted on going on stage last winter in the Inkbarrow Vale production despite having broken her hip, her wrist and her left ankle in a skiing accident."

"Very brave of her," Rachel commented. "Did she get away with it?"

"Well, it was certainly the most novel interpretation of the *Dance Of The Sugar Plum Fairy* I've ever seen," said Ken.

Sunday 9th November

It was good to see Ruth back with us for what proved to be a moving and inspiring Remembrance Day service. The vicar asked us to be sure to switch off our mobile phones to avoid a breach of the Two Minutes' Silence at the town's war memorial; a request which unfortunately proved somewhat unnecessary, since even the most intrusive ring tone would have been drowned out, as our preceding motet *Thou Knowest Lord* was, by the Savemart delivery lorry that passed by at exactly the same time.

Afterwards, Ruth summoned together the drama group members, and told us that there were two bits of good news: firstly, she has two if not three, people to audition to take her place in the play, and secondly that there are not only posters but also handbills and car stickers available for promoting the production. The fact that at present it appears we will probably be forced to perform in the church hall committee room, with seating capacity for eleven, is apparently something that we need not be entirely candid about.

Was more than a little surprised by the keenness with which Matthew Sparkes snapped up a good seventy per cent of the car stickers. As I understood it, they were a one-car family and although I don't know what Alison's husband does for a living, he has certainly never struck me as your archetypal second-hand motor trader. I thought no more of it, however, and went round to Katie's to enjoy a delicious Sunday lunch before our afternoon play rehearsal. Was in excellent spirits as I drove on to Ruth's house, and my mood was further improved when Ruth told me we had received a free plug for our play on local radio. Less ecstatic when I was informed that the mention for the play was in the context of a complaint to the police by residents of Torrington Road to the effect that they were unable to use their cars, owing to lengths of our advertising material being fastened to at least twelve front windscreens with superglue.

To my surprise, Tripplehorn came along this afternoon on the pretext of wanting to give the convalescing Ruth some encouragement and offer some support. He sat through the bits we were able to rehearse, appeared to be tittering in all the right places, and listened very sympathetically while we explained our difficulties in finding a replacement for Ruth and also a suitable alternative venue for the production.

"I know just the place for you to perform," he said. "It's very inexpensive to hire, it's exceedingly flexible, the seats for the audience are really very comfortable, by using it you would be being as faithful as possible to your avowed aim of bringing theatre to the community and making it easily accessible for all, and its size reflects the level of popular support you deserve to enjoy."

"Oh, yes, where's that?" I asked him.

"The back of my brother's camper van," he replied.

Tuesday 11th November

It's an ill wind. The publicity for our play on local radio, inadvertently generated by Matthew's antisocial adhesive antics, provided a basis for Ruth to approach the radio station again today and request them to put out an appeal for a new venue. And at tonight's rehearsal we were informed that Lord and Lady Buttermere have agreed to host the play in the Great Hall of Wintersgill, their magnificent home on the edge of town. Although there is no stage in the Great Hall, the room is spacious enough to permit the erection of tiered seating, which has been arranged through a contact of Lord Buttermere's in Salisbury. Volunteers will be needed on the Sunday before to assist in preparing the hall, and we will then have up to five nights to rehearse in the hall itself before curtain up on the Friday night. In the meantime, we will continue to rehearse at Ruth's home on Tuesday evenings.

Quite apart from choosing someone to take Ruth's place, which will be done on Sunday night, we still have the problem of selling the tickets. "Drastic situations call for drastic measures," said Ruth Hartnell. "Here's fifteen tickets each. Four for family members, the others for friends, neighbours, butchers, bakers, candlestick makers, anybody. I want each and every one of them sold by Sunday. If they aren't, we cancel the show." She then called a halt to tonight's rehearsal at eight forty five, announced that the promised flapjacks and chocolate brownies were off the menu, and told us to go home and start phoning.

I wouldn't have wished the hour that followed on my worst enemy. Having rung every acquaintance of mine within a radius of eighty miles, and got just four positive responses, I actually found myself reduced to ringing everyone on my street, using the relevant parts of the electoral register I'd managed to purloin from work. I was taking a bit of a risk, as I guessed I was almost certainly violating the Data Protection Act and whatever provision of the Human Rights Convention it is that gives the

162

subject an inalienable right to watch *Big Brother* free from interruption of any kind. And having undertaken the task, I can't now think either of a better training exercise for a budding telesales operative, or richer material for the as yet unpublished book listing a hundred ways to deal with one. Of the thirty numbers I tried before reaching for the Valium, eight hung up the moment I said "I'm so sorry to trouble you," five brusquely interrupted with the words "Not interested" and slammed the phone down, six told me they'd registered with the Telephone Preference Service *ergo* I had no business bothering them at all, a few listened to my whole spiel and then pretended they'd not heard a single word I'd said, and one lady asked if I could call back some other time as she and her husband were at that precise moment leaving their house for the last time prior to their emigration to southern Australia.

My big breakthrough came at the end of the evening when the charming man at number 78 told me he'd be delighted to come along to the matinee performance and would be bringing at least ten others with him. Joyfully I took a note of all his details, made arrangements for the provision of tickets and the payment of the ticket monies, and replaced the receiver, delighted that I had fulfilled Ruth's requirements.

It was only as I was making my coffee a few minutes later that the realisation hit me. That we aren't actually doing a matinee.

Friday 14th November

Quite a lot of time spent at choir tonight on the music for the two big services this month, namely the wedding on the Saturday and the confirmation eight days later. The couple getting married have asked for two modern choruses and although Tripplehorn had to have his statutory sneer at them, I did really enjoy rehearsing them this evening. As we were singing the second chorus, I noticed that Margaret was clearly entering into the spirit of the thing in every sense, dispensing with her music and looking heavenwards, her eyes tight shut and her right hand raised. It was quite moving to see her depth of spiritual commitment although I confess it did make me feel rather inadequate. Tripplehorn looked somewhat perplexed but thankfully kept a diplomatic silence and it was left to Hazel Ledworthy to mutter "I do wish that girl would remember that we are in a house of God."

Tripplehorn did, however, have some stern words for the play participants afterwards, telling us that Savemart lorry or no Savemart lorry, *Thou Knowest Lord* at the war memorial last Sunday had been a shambles, and the cause of it was the fact that we thespians had been away with the fairies; consequently we're to pull up our socks, knuckle down, toe the line and get the ship back on course on future Sundays. I don't suppose Thomas Beecham could have put it any more succinctly.

When I returned from choir there was a message on my answering machine to phone back a work acquaintance, George Elfinstow, one of the many people with whom I'd left messages on Tuesday night. The message was to the effect that he was interested in my play and could I tell him more about it. I felt I had no alternative but to ring him back, notwithstanding that Katie was with me this evening and had told me supper, for which I was ravenous, would be on the table in ten minutes. Which made it exceptionally irritating for her, and no more pleasurable for me, that twenty minutes later I should find myself being quizzed extensively by George Elfinstow about the plot, the characterisations, the scenery and in fact almost every detail of the production, from the material used for the curtains across the stage to the farm providing the milk for the interval teas and coffees. Believing myself to be on to a winner, I spoke at length about the rigorous attention to detail during rehearsals, the professionalism and commitment of the cast, the quality of the writing and the determination and enthusiasm of those constructing the set and assembling the props, lavishing so much praise on all these aspects that by the time I had finished I was even beginning to convince myself. I then asked him how many tickets he would like.

"Oh, I won't be able to go," he said. "I'm in Pennsylvania that week."

On a one-way ticket, I hope.

Sunday 16ᵗʰ November

Katie's last service before her confirmation, as she'll be away next Sunday. She was prayed for by name, along with the six other confirmation candidates, during the intercessions. After Tripplehorn's stinging words to us at Friday's rehearsal, we sang the anthem, Clarke-Whitfeld's *Behold How Good And Joyful*, very well indeed. And for the recession we sang *Love Divine* to Blaenwern, which I have always regarded as infinitely more enjoyable to sing than Stainer's four-line tune that was written for this hymn.

It was Hazel Ledworthy's 70ᵗʰ birthday today and there was celebratory fruit cake provided in the body of the church hall afterwards. It seemed to me to be an ideal opportunity to clear the air with her, so I made a point of going over to her, wishing her many happy returns and telling her what a delicious piece of fruit cake it was. To my surprise and delight, she smiled and thanked me for my kind words. Now on something of a roll, I said to her "Lovely, that last hymn, wasn't it?"

"Yes," she replied. "I asked for it myself."

"Very good choice," I said, "and so much better than that awfully drab Stainer tune."

"That was actually the one I thought I'd asked the organist for," Hazel replied frostily.

Ah well. I'll just have to try again when she hits eighty.

Tonight we held auditions for Ruth's part in the play, and somewhat to my surprise, I was asked to join Ruth on the auditioning committee. As I expected, the two candidates were indeed Florence Muxworth and Elspeth Dewberry. Florence was first to audition. Even before she opened her mouth to begin her audition piece she went through a litany of reasons for the dreadfulness of the audition she was about to give, ranging from the toothache suffered by her sister-in-law's great aunt's next door neighbour a week ago last Tuesday to the unforeseen attack of vermin on her bilberry plants. Elspeth Dewberry began by providing a typewritten curriculum vitae of every stage play and performance in which she had taken part, from the key role of First Courtier in the West Harwich Junior School Class Eight production of *The Emperor's New Clothes* in 1947, to Sitti Ping in the "magnificently acclaimed" premiere of *Not The Mikado* by Selwyn Aspinwall in the conference room of the Mayflower Road Social Club, Blackpool, in 1975. It was hard to know which was the more ghastly offering but mindful we had to make a decision on it, we sat from twenty past nine until nearly eleven o'clock weighing up the pros and cons of each, finally agreeing that the psychological damage done to the distressed owner of blighted fruit crops must inevitably affect his or her ability to deliver when called upon to do so, and therefore the doyenne of post-war West Harwich school drama should be given the vacant role.

Staggered home and had just put the kettle on for a well-earned cup of strong coffee when the telephone rang. It was Ruth. "I've had another think," she said. "I've decided to rewrite my part on the basis that the character is supposed to have her foot in plaster as part of the play. That means I can do it. I think it'll be easier all round."

And there I was thinking I'd missed *Heartbeat* for nothing.

Tuesday 18th November

Our penultimate rehearsal at Ruth's. It was a good rehearsal: everybody seemed up for it tonight, and Ruth's performance was in many ways more humorous and entertaining than it had been when she had enjoyed the full uninterrupted use of her lower limbs. Over delicious home-made carrot cake that followed, Ruth asked if we'd sold the allocations of tickets we'd been given.

"I've now got rid of all mine for Saturday," said Rachel, "but Friday is proving problematic. I can't seem to sell any for the Friday at all."

"I'm the same," said Matthew. "All my friends are coming Saturday."

"I should have all my Saturday allocation sold tomorrow at bridge," said Cora, "but I think everyone I've asked says they're fully booked on Friday."

Ken then reported that of those he had managed to persuade to come, all bar one was for Saturday night. And on enquiry from Ruth I had to advise that my ticket sales followed an identical pattern.

"This is ridiculous," Ruth barked, not even bothering to ask Arthur Ramsbottom who, as was his custom when she was on the warpath, was busy mingling with her shelf-full of Harpers and Queens. "Is there another function going on in town on the Friday night that I don't know anything about?"

"I think it's the night of the Mayor's Grand Ball in the Town Hall," said Rachel. "His last big charity function during his term of office."

"In aid of what?" Ruth enquired.

"I think it's the St Leodegar's School Minibus Appeal," said Rachel.

"Well, no wonder so many people are booked up that night," Ruth said angrily. "Did someone not check that there were no rival functions on in town that evening?"

"I believed we checked with Joan Trumpington, who knows about these things," said Rachel. "Although, I must say, she didn't really seem quite with it."

Infuriating though this news was, I thought it somewhat ungracious of Ruth to slam her half-eaten slice of carrot cake on to the table in such a marked manner. Surely she of all people should know that the nearest Joan Trumpington has ever been to "it" is Row X seat 149.

Friday 21st November

A super choir practice tonight, consisting of a runthrough of the lovely music for the weekend wedding and confirmation services, and a good canter through the relatively straightforward second half of the play evenings, consisting of carols for choir and audience. I was also able to report that known sales of Arthur's book have now crawled up to one hundred, meaning we are halfway to breaking even. But afterwards, we had to hold an emergency meeting to decide whether to try and shift the first night of the play to the Thursday, to cancel it altogether or to keep it on Friday and hope that we will get an audience of more than the two ushers, three tea ladies and my next door neighbour but four, Doris Kirk-Whelpington.

"Why don't you make Friday the dress rehearsal night?" Henry Peasgood suggested. "That way, if there are people watching, it gives you the feeling of working with an audience."

"Seems an awful lot of work just for one night's performance," said Alison. "Have you thought about a Saturday matinee?"

"Well, I wouldn't be seen dead attending a matinee and if anyone's got any sense they won't either," said Irving Cattermole. "Horrible kids with runny noses darting in and out of the seats, raddled nonagenarians snoring directly in front of you, performers wishing they were doing something else a hundred miles away, and coachloads of mental defectives shipped in from the local loony bins blundering about the place believing themselves to be on the 95 bus to Ponders End."

"You put up with all that here every Sunday morning," Tripplehorn reminded him. "Ruth, it's up to you."

"And my decision," said Ruth, "is that we proceed on the Friday night as planned and redouble our efforts to sell tickets. This town can support more than one charity function on one night. Mayoral functions aren't the be all and end all of this community. And I can tell you from personal experience that there's nothing particularly special about the Mayor's balls."

There's no answer to that.

Saturday 22nd November

Today was the big wedding, with a full choir attendance. I must say the whole affair was very splendid indeed; the whole church was lit by candles, with the service timed for 4.30pm to enhance the effect, and all the male guests wore morning suits. The organisation that had gone into the thing was clearly enormous. So it must have come as a bitter blow to those in charge of the timings to be told that the whole ceremony would have to be delayed by up to an hour and a half because the bride's best friend had been delayed by fog on her flight down from Glasgow.

We found this out just as we were about to process into church, and immediately upon hearing the news, Hazel Ledworthy and Irving Cattermole began to disrobe. "I'm sorry, but I'm not prepared to wait an hour and a half," said Irving. "I've better things to do with my Saturday evening."

Tripplehorn waited until they had walked out and closed the door behind them, then said "Good, we can start to make some music now." He opened the vestry cupboard, distributed a large heap of anthems amongst us, went out to the waiting congregation and told them to stay put and enjoy "the choir of St Basil's by candlelight," ushered us in and announced the first piece. The time certainly passed quickly, and the punters did appear to be enjoying the experience, but I was glad Tripplehorn had had the foresight to produce as many anthems as he did, for when the service eventually got under way, we had just two anthems left to do. Probably just as well that one of the unused ones was Percy Luffington's piece based on part of Psalm 40, *Make No Long Tarrying, O My God.*

When the service, which proved to be every bit as moving and enjoyable as I hoped, finally came to an end, we had a lovely surprise. Because of all the extra singing we'd done, we were given a cheque for the vestry fund representing two and a half times the amount originally promised. "And there's more good news," said Tripplehorn. "The chairman of the town's chamber of commerce was in the congregation and he liked our singing so much that he's promised us a slot in the market square carols on December 14th. It should make us a lot of money."

I had mixed feelings about this. December 14th is a Sunday. It will be the first time that the town, which generally speaking is dead as a dodo on Sundays, has seen most if not all of its shops open on the day of rest. Apparently if the experiment, which will run for the three Sundays in December prior to Christmas, is successful, it is possible that Sunday opening will become the norm in the New Year. Unsurprisingly, not everyone is happy about the scheme and I am one of those who isn't. I'm a great believer in the special nature of Sunday and the importance of keeping one day a week apart from the rest, primarily for the purpose of worship but also for the promotion of family togetherness. I do appreciate that, with sales of Arthur's book moving somewhat ponderously, we need a further boost for the vestry funds, but despite the lateness of the hour I couldn't resist querying the ethics of our being involved.

Lesley however had no such qualms. "Just think," she said. "It may mean we don't have to do one of these ghastly evenings round the town, banging on people's doors and getting either soaking wet or frozen stiff in the process. At least the part of the square we'd sing from would be under cover."

"I always rather look forward to evening carol-singing," said Alison.

"You obviously weren't with us the year before last," said Lesley, "when we sang three carols outside a house in Didcot Drive only for the door to open to reveal four black-suited men bearing the dead body of the sole occupier out with them."

"Or the year before that," said Ken, "when we'd just sung the words 'all is calm, all is bright' when there was a massive clap of thunder and a gust of wind which whipped Miranda Cobbledick's music from her hand and sent it flying into the main road to be crushed by a passing National Express coach bound for Budleigh Salterton."

Perhaps this Sunday opening isn't such a bad thing after all.

Sunday 23rd November

In the absence of the vicar, who was preaching elsewhere this morning, today's service was taken by one Walter Collington whom I'd never seen before at St Basil's. To begin with he looked destined to join the long list of celebrants who had found their way on to Tripplehorn's blacklist. Announcing the anthem, which we performed barely adequately, as *Lift Up Your Gates O Ye Heads* by Mathias Williams, praying for the swift healing of two old ladies who'd passed away three weeks ago, and suggesting the first Advent candle be lit despite the fact that Advent didn't start till next week, were just a few of his gems of absent-mindedness. But the moment he started preaching, he was electrifying. Taking as his theme "community," he launched into a quite magnificent diatribe about the total selfishness of our culture, neglecting as we did the notion of family solidarity and failing to integrate ourselves truly and wholeheartedly into the community around us. "We gloat at the appalling behaviour of our soap stars and the villains of reality TV," he said, "yet can we condone any more our own reclining in our armchairs when there are wounded lives just seconds from our front door?" And to my amazement and delight, he referred, by way of an example, to the "appalling and abysmal" response to the play advertising. "This is a play by your community for your community," he went on. "It not only deserves your support. It requires it. There is no option. God will forgive us many things. He will not forgive us neglecting those around us." As a result of his fine words, we sold a further fifteen tickets for the Friday and are now completely sold out for the Saturday.

During coffee afterwards I went up to Ruth and said to her "You must be absolutely thrilled with that sermon this morning."

"Yes, he delivered it well," Ruth replied in businesslike fashion. "As chief vestry fund raiser, do you think it could have been improved upon?"

Somewhat nonplussed, I replied "Not really. Perhaps a bit more emphasis on where the money was going. That's all."

"Good. Just what I thought," said Ruth. She opened her handbag and withdrew two pages of paper which contained the typed text of the entire sermon. "To be honest," she went on, "When I wrote it I wasn't terribly happy with the last couple of paragraphs on page one. I'll amend it on my PC tonight in time for him to deliver the same sermon to the Monday Afternoon Julian Group in the Methodist Church tomorrow. There are still a lot of empty seats for the first night."

Tuesday 25th November

Following a competent rehearsal for the play, we were invited round to Lord Buttermere's house at Wintersgill in order to get the feel of the place and to work out how the Great Hall will be set up for next week.

All seems to be in order, and Lord Buttermere was a charming host, laughing off Matthew's leaning against a fine bone china plate causing it to smash to a thousand pieces, and telling us he'd long disliked the thing and could happily use the insurance money. The Great Hall did, however, feel very cold; the high ceilings and lack of insulation mean that even central heating fails to give the room any significant warmth in the depths of winter. Now I understand what Phyllis Muggleton meant when she asked if free hot water bottles are issued with the tickets. I was slightly alarmed also that, despite the fact that Wintersgill is just on the outskirts of town, to get to it involves a drive up a steep pot-holed lane and although there is a reasonably spacious forecourt it can only accommodate twelve vehicles. I mentioned this to Ruth as we were leaving afterwards.

"Oh, there's a large field just round the side," she said. "The audience can use that. It can get a bit waterlogged. And it's rather overgrown in places. And the access isn't all that easy. And there's no security lighting, of course."

"Do you think I ought to check it out this evening?" I queried.

"If you want," said Ruth. "But you'll have to get the bull out of it first."

I'm sure it'll be fine.

Friday 28th November

A lovely choir practice tonight, cantering through the music for the play evenings and then putting the final polish on Sunday's confirmation service music. I do agree with Tripplehorn that even though the calendar year is still not at an end, Advent is like a fresh start as we begin a new Church Year with its wonderful contrasts of light, shade, sadness, joy, contemplation and exuberance.

We talked more about the carol-singing two weeks on Sunday. I'm not the only one who is unhappy about the situation. Predictably Margaret has said she wishes no part in it, Eileen Crosby has said she regards it as morally questionable, and Hazel Ledworthy was making adverse mutterings too, not that there is anything unusual about that.

"Well," said Tripplehorn when the debate has run its course. "Of course, I think this Sunday opening business is disgraceful."

I was quite touched that our choirmaster, not normally one for taking the moral high ground on any ethical matter, should speak out so forcefully in favour of the true Christian position on this most delicate of issues.

Until, that is, he went on "I've always had the Goat And Compasses to myself for my Sunday roast. Now I shan't be able to move for sweaty shoppers in tawdry tracksuits and tatty trainers."

Advent Sunday 30th November

Katie's confirmation service this morning.

I must say I don't think I can ever recall enjoying a service in St Basil's quite as much as I did today. The church was packed, and there were lots of young people including some I recognised as having attended at Harvest for the first time. The music, which included some of my favourite Advent hymns, was super, and Tripplehorn congratulated us all afterwards. Katie looked absolutely gorgeous. In fact, I thought she'd never looked lovelier. There was a huge lump in my throat when I saw her take communion for the first time in her life, having been totally indifferent to spiritual matters less than a year ago. Margaret took me aside afterwards and said "I've never seen such joy in your eyes as I saw this morning. You've served God so faithfully in raising money this year for the vestry. Now He is rewarding you a hundredfold." It was all I could do not to start blubbing.

Sadly anticlimax set in after a huge pub lunch with Katie's parents and her two sisters, as I had to be round at Wintersgill for three o'clock to assist with the setting-up of the Great Hall in readiness for our technical rehearsal this evening. I arrived, somewhat breathless, at two minutes past three, having had to wolf down my far from digestible treacle sponge pudding and custard. Because of a delay to the van that was transporting the staging and seating, it wasn't till five past five that we were able to start work; the technical rehearsal, timed for 5.30, had to be put back until 7; and instead of being away by half past seven as hoped, I was still there at nearly nine o'clock. We all did our best to while away the enforced idleness. I had taken the precaution of bringing with me the *Shires Weekend Echo* Jumbo 154-clue cryptic prize crossword. Arthur decided it might be quite a good idea to look at some of his lines. Speaking extremely loudly and at considerable length on her mobile phone, Cora was holding a virtual meeting of the Quiet Group Committee. And Matthew succeeded where countless generations of Buttermeres had failed by finding the right way to remove the armrest from a priceless Queen Anne upright dining chair.

No sign of Jane. Again. Probably just as well, in some ways; if I am supposed to infer, as Margaret has suggested, that God has blessed my relationship with Katie so strongly, it wouldn't do to start getting mixed messages from on high by the appearance, on today of all days, of Katie's principal rival for my affections. Apparently she will be with us on Tuesday. I'll believe that when I see it.

We somehow staggered through to the end of the technical, but with probably more issues to resolve next time than there had been at the start. It looks as if Tuesday will be a long night. Entrances and exits were not where we expected them, the scenery was incomplete, anyone setting foot on the wooden stage flooring with hard-soled shoes sent shock waves all round the room of such magnitude as to register on the Richter scale, and the hall itself seemed even colder than it had done on Tuesday. Ruth, evidently totally frustrated by her enforced immobility, got more and more irritable as the evening went on, and it did not take a Masters degree in psychology to gather that it would be best not to bother her with any unnecessary or peripheral issues. So it was left to Arthur Ramsbottom, blessed with the diplomatic and empathetic skills of a deep-fried turbot, to blunder up to her as we were all getting our coats on at the end of the evening, and say to her "What about my coming out before the play starts, welcoming the audience and giving them a sneak preview of the choir book?"

"I wouldn't if I were you," said Ruth, "that is, if you're actually hoping people will want to buy it."

Her sarcasm was completely lost on Arthur. "Oh, I see," he said. "You mean if I give away too much people will think they might as well not buy it at all because I'm bound to have told them the best bits in advance."

"Just go home, Arthur," said Ruth.

DECEMBER

Tuesday 2nd December

Our penultimate rehearsal for the play. On Thursday the full choir join us to go through the second half of the evening's entertainment, making it effectively a runthrough of the complete programme.

It seemed colder at Wintersgill than ever tonight. Despite the fact that the radiators and the extra heaters we had brought in were going full blast, there were still pockets of the room that possessed the iciness of the welcome a deputation of Colorado beetles could expect at the Potato Farmers Association end-of-season banquet. "And it's going to get worse by the weekend," Cora warned. "My son-in-law told me on the phone tonight. We may get quite a lot of snow. It could make access to Wintersgill pretty well impossible."

"It never snows any more," said Rachel. "Global warming and all that. What does he know?"

"Quite a lot," said Cora, "as he happens to be a senior meteorologist at Bristol Weather Centre."

At last, Jane turned up tonight. After the wonderful experience of Katie's confirmation on Sunday, I'd wondered how I would react when she came in. To begin with, I must say I felt intense irritation. It was obvious she'd hardly looked at the part at all, and she seemed to have no compunction about walking around the stage with her book in her hand for those all too frequent occasions when she forgot what she was meant to say next, and reciting the lines in a lifeless fashion suggesting little or no effort to get under the skin of the character. Admittedly, her acting was probably no worse than Arthur's, and her movement inevitably rather more graceful than Ruth's, but I saw no call for Ruth to be quite so forgiving or tolerant of her lack of preparation while being so unnecessarily harsh on other cast members, Matthew particularly. I guessed why Matthew had come in for such vituperative comment. But then if people will leave spotless two hundred year old tiger skin rugs so close to where super-concentrate blackcurrant Ribena is being consumed, they must face the consequences. By the time we'd reached our love scene towards the end, however, my attitude towards Jane had certainly mellowed. During the very necessary coffee break, she'd told me that although she was feeling tired tonight after travelling for most of the day, she was looking forward to going with me for a drink after Thursday's rehearsal. And although my loyalty to Katie was never in serious danger of being compromised – well, not tonight anyway – I was very much looking forward to our moment of passion halfway down page 53. Certainly Jane's baggy jumper, trousers and gym shoes did not present as the most stunning outfit in which I'd seen her, and she admitted that having eaten a garlic mushroom pizza

with double portion of garlic bread she felt it best to be, in her words, "economical in the snog department." I don't wish to take anything away from Margaret, who has been such a devoted understudy over the past couple of months. But I fear that in terms of making me feel more comfortable about my role, and indeed the play itself, there was simply no contest between her hideous wet slobbery kisses over the preceding weeks and what were mere token pecks that Jane planted on my cheek tonight. Notwithstanding the pungent aroma of Pizza A Go Go produce hanging unappetisingly in the air.

Thursday 4th December

Ruth rang me at work this morning to say she's managed to get us a slot on the local BBC radio station at 9.45 tonight to be interviewed about the play and asked if I could please do the interview and also phone the BBC to confirm the arrangement and my arrival time. However, as I'd made arrangements to meet Jane after rehearsal tonight, I decided somebody else could jolly well do the radio interview – thoughts of which were in any event banished from my mind when I chanced to hear two work colleagues speaking about the weather outlook. It seems on Saturday we can indeed expect some quite significant snowfalls.

Whether or not it was unease about the forecast I don't know, but tonight's dress rehearsal wasn't a success and the cold was almost unbearable. Lord Buttermere even went as far as to invite us into his drawing room in the tea interval and warm ourselves in front of his log fire, which was burning even more fiercely than usual with the addition of the wooden curtain pole that Matthew had presciently broken into three pieces earlier in the evening. As had been promised, we ran it as a performance and after a pep talk from both Ruth and Tripplehorn we were free by 9.30. Jane, who was dressed to kill in a low-cut top and very short skirt, turned to me as soon as we were dismissed and said "Are we going for it then, lover boy?" No second invitation was needed; heedless of any other demands on my time I swept out of the room and minutes later found myself drawing up outside Jane's chosen location. It wasn't a cosy country pub, as I'd hoped, but a nightclub situated on one of the town's outlying industrial estates. Jane, however, promised me that I would love it. I began to have my doubts about that as soon as we entered the foyer to be greeted by a gaggle of youths whom she unashamedly announced as a group of her mates from university and whom she had apparently planned to meet at this time. There was Taz, sporting a blue plastic ear-ring and grubby T-shirt inviting readers to Smash The Pigs; Baz, who had a spiky choker round his neck and a passable Eddie Waring impersonation; Chaz, who wore a long faded trench coat with khaki shorts and knee-high New Rock boots; and Yaz, who came complete with

Che Guevara tattoo, ripped jeans and flipflops. Faced with these seekers after sartorial excellence and being quickly made aware that I had as much chance in competing with them for Jane's affections that night as the club's emblematic pink rubber rabbit that was hanging by its earlobes from the ceiling directly above the door to the gents' toilet, I decided enough was enough. Making an excuse to Baz and ignoring an insulting remark from Taz, I edged my way past Yaz and Chaz, hurried back to my car and drove home.

When I got in I found a message on my answering machine from the evening producer on the BBC local radio station querying why I hadn't attended for interview tonight. It seemed that Ruth had rung the BBC and had made out it was all their fault, so despite the lateness of the hour, I rang them back and offered my humble apologies. The producer thankfully couldn't have been nicer about it. "There again," I said, "I'm not sure we'd have sold any more tickets even if it had gone on air."

"Oh, you'd be surprised," the producer replied. "Our Thursday night arts slot is one of the most popular programmes on our station. Thankfully we had a standby item and I'm sure the organisation that came on instead will be most grateful."

"Who were they?" I asked.

"The St Leodegar's School Minibus Appeal," said the producer.

I was too wound up to turn in for the night so after a cup of coffee I washed a couple of shirts. In Daz.

Friday 5th December

Rang up Ruth as soon as I got into work to apologise profusely for last night and asking if there was anything I could do to make amends in terms of promoting tonight and tomorrow night's performances. "I suppose there is something," she said. "It wouldn't involve anything more strenuous than wandering round town for a while and you wouldn't have to say or do anything else at all. If you pop round this morning I should have it all ready for you."

"Have what ready?" I asked her.

"Two blank white sandwich boards and a pot of red paint," she replied.

I'd sooner lick the cobwebs off Lord Buttermere's dado rails.

Half an hour later, after graciously declining Ruth's suggestion, I had Lesley on the phone telling me that thanks to "a certain person who shall remain nameless" going AWOL from the Red Bunny Club last night, Jane had had to make her own way home on foot through sub-zero temperatures. As a result she was now nursing what she believed to be a severe chill and could not possibly go on stage tonight. I will admit that I felt really rather bad about having let her down the way I had. Until, that is, I chanced to meet one of her cronies from last night while queuing in the post office at lunchtime. I mentioned to him that Jane was under the weather today, to which he replied "Well, she certainly didn't seem so good when we poured her out of the taxi at her house at half three this morning."

"So she didn't walk home, then," I said.

"Walk?" he echoed. "After her ninth double vodka she could barely climb the steps out of the bar. On all fours."

I phoned Ruth again to ask if she was aware of the latest developments. "Yes," she said. "And Margaret Pardew has said she'll be delighted to do the part." I can't say I share her delight. But then again, at that precise moment I couldn't really have cared whether Jane's part was being taken by Margaret Pardew, the vice chairman of the Edgell Street Over 80's Club or the Hag Queen of Haselbury Plucknett.

The weathermen are now divided as to whether we will get the snow tomorrow after all. Jenny Sutcliffe on Nick Axeltree's BBC Drivetime show seems to think we might escape. Nigel Pietrusiewicz, on Rustic FM's Teatime Treats, was less optimistic. But if we thought that the prospect of snow tomorrow might place more backsides on seats tonight, we were sadly mistaken. And whether we make any profit on the evening at all will depend on a number of things:

Firstly, whether the two old ladies sitting in the front row will pursue a claim for damages for post-traumatic stress disorder after being torn off a strip by Cora Willoughby-Smith in the tea interval for unwrapping a family pack of Revels just as she was beginning her key speech at the top of page 37.

Secondly, whether Lord Buttermere will take a lenient view of Matthew's adlibbed prank of carrying on to the set, and unzipping, a snake-shaped door stop and inundating the stage with minute pieces of white polystyrene.

Thirdly, whether we receive a bill for hospital treatment and costs of reheeling a pair of stilettos from the middle-aged woman who slipped through a grille in the east wing passageway leading to the basement having been assured by Joan Trumpington that that really was the quickest way to the second floor ladies' conveniences.

Fourthly, whether our overworked and grossly undervalued prompt files a claim for special overtime pay for effectively reciting the whole of pages 6, 7 and 8 when Arthur Ramsbottom jumped spectacularly from the middle of page 5 to somewhere down page 19, doing a back flip to page 11 and then leaping forward to a small sheep farm about 30 kilometres north-east of Wagga Wagga.

And finally, whether there is any insurance policy in the possession of Ruth Hartnell, the church or indeed anybody else which might cover the cost of replacing the hot air blower, hired at enormous expense from A1

Electrics earlier today, which took it upon itself to explode during the carols, scattering metal over a wide area, singeing the bottom of Prudence Taylorson's cashmere jacket and putting Lady Buttermere's chihuahua off its savoury nuts until further notice.

Saturday 6th December

We gathered at Ruth's this morning for an an extraordinary meeting to decide what to do about tonight. We could cancel, and claim a proportion of the refunded ticket money off insurance; we could move the performance to another more central venue; or we could gamble on the snow staying away and remain at Wintersgill for the performance, knowing that if snow set in it would make both access and parking quite impossible.

"It really does look like snow," said Ken. "The sky's that steely grey colour and it's not quite as cold this morning. That's a sure sign."

"The Bristol Met Office radar points to it arriving in our area mid-afternoon," said Cora.

"We will be getting snow this evening definitely," said Arthur. "My source is quite definite on that point."

"And which source would this be, Arthur, my love?" Ruth enquired. "Bearnaise, HP, or Birds Eye Boil in the Bag Cod In Butter?"

Arthur did not flinch. "My friend Brian up on the slopes of Inkbarrow saw flakes swirling around the back of his house at first light," he said, "and that's always the precursor to a big snowfall by evening."

Surprisingly, Ken backed Arthur up. "I've never known Brian proved wrong," he said. "I think we need to take this seriously, Ruth."

"Very well," said Ruth with a sigh. "The church hall it is. I checked last night and it is still free. We'll have to use the well of the hall and sit people round the edge. I'll try and get something on the radio and ring everyone I know who's got tickets. Rachel, if you can find out from everyone else who they're expecting to come and let me have the names. Arthur, will you please organise a sign by the entrance to Wintersgill. And the rest of you, plus Arthur when you've done the sign, you need to start shifting scenery and props from the Wintersgill stage and round to the hall. I'll see if I can get a van hire firm to cart the heavier stuff."

Thankfully the snow held off as Arthur, Ken, Cora, Margaret and I drove to Lord Buttermere's home and loaded our respective vehicles with as much as we could take. Matthew proved to be a great little worker and thanks to his industry and energy the job was completed in next to no time. But his last load, comprising mostly a selection of worthless props Arthur had snapped up at a car boot sale last month, proved a mite too ambitious, for as he marched out of the door towards my car I saw a rather vulgar carriage clock fall off the top of the pile he was carrying and crash down on to the ice-cold concrete below. I didn't suppose Arthur would miss it.

Ruth joined us at the hall after lunch and directed operations as we set about putting up what scenery we could. But although we did our best, the whole thing still looked rather makeshift. We weren't helped by the number of interruptions. Firstly from a rather officious policeman, telling us that our sign outside the entrance to Wintersgill warning patrons of the change of venue was causing an obstruction, and would whoever had erected it kindly put it out of harm's way. Secondly from Mr Pockett the caretaker telling us that the positioning of audience chairs all round the hall including in front of a designated fire door violated the Brussels Convention On Health And Safety, prompting a response from Ruth that those chairs were staying put and she didn't care if she was violating the Brussels Convention, the European Convention, the Weak No Trump Convention or Fairport Convention. And thirdly from Lord Buttermere enquiring about the whereabouts of his 19th century handcarved Mexican timepiece recently valued at auction at £25,000.

After addressing all these various matters, there was only just time for us to pop home, freshen up and glean from the local radio weather report that the snow having motored confidently towards us down the A303 had taken an abrupt left turn at Upper Clatford and after a pause for refreshment at King's Somborne was now heading out into the Channel, missing us altogether.

Had we got the job done quicker we might just have had time to reinstate the final night at Wintersgill as planned. But by the time I'd collapsed on to the settee, totally exhausted, for ten well-earned minutes in front of *Celebrity Dog Walking Challenge*, any thought of altering the venue once more was about as palatable as the meat pies on offer at Mr Tasty's in Greville Road immediately before the execution of last week's warrants of entry to the premises under the Food Safety Act.

It was hardly surprising that the happy anticipation which should have preceded the final night of a show for which we'd been practising for months was replaced by a sense of dejected anticlimax combined with fury that our decision had proved to be so wrong. The hall was at least warmer than Wintersgill – I don't think we could have made it any colder than Wintersgill if we'd tried – but the pathetic array of scenery hastily culled from Lord Buttermere's and placed somewhat haphazardly round the centre of the hall, the two tight rows of chairs crammed round three sides, and the backcloth of dust sheets protecting the unusable stage, was hardly likely to encourage the paying customers to engage with the action. Not that there were a lot of customers in any event. A number whom we'd phoned had already assumed the play was off and had made other plans. Jane was still poorly and her not inconsiderable entourage decided not to bother to see what Margaret made of the part in her absence. At least three people said they'd only reserved tickets because they wanted to see a play being performed in Wintersgill and for no other reason. And a good percentage of the rest appeared not to have been aware of the change of venue at all. Worse, the majority of the non-attenders hadn't paid for their tickets in advance. With morale amongst all of us at rock bottom, we stumbled along to the end of the play, just willing the wretched thing to finish. The relief when it finally did so was palpable, not only amongst the cast but the feeble audience. Katie was there, and even she was moved to say that she had experienced more excitement and enjoyment at her school chiropodist's annual verruca inspections.

There followed a coffee interval before the carols for choir and audience. As I slurped my hot drink, I noticed a man and a woman arriving, so, with Ruth and Arthur looking on, I welcomed them and told them I was sorry they'd missed the play.

"We've done well to get here at all," the man replied somewhat coolly. "I think ours was the only car that escaped from the pile-up at Wintersgill in a driveable state."

"Pile-up!" I echoed back at him.

"A major pile-up," he told me. "Someone coming back down the Wintersgill drive having just found the play had been moved smashed head on into a car coming up the drive and the convoy of cars behind each of them just ploughed into the mess. We had to fight our way past two police cars, a fire engine and at least five tow trucks just to get back to the main road."

"So nobody saw the sign at the entrance advertising the change of venue?" I asked him.

"What sign?" he queried.

Instinctively both Ruth and I looked round to Arthur but he had disappeared. And with Ruth's face having turned the colour of the raspberryade being served at that moment to Constance Gimblett, I can't say I blame him for wanting to conceal himself from her as effectively as possible. Either by booking a one-way ticket to the Galapagos Islands. Or finding one of the mustier corners of Mr Pockett's basement tool closet.

Sunday 7th December

I think any one of us, especially those who took part in the play, could have been forgiven for staying in bed this morning, and I was quite surprised at how few were missing from the choir for Advent 2 and our usual thirty two verses of *O Come O Come Emmanuel* plus the first verse repeated at the end for good measure. I wasn't altogether surprised that Arthur was absent this morning. As we disrobed afterwards, I remarked to Ken that had he turned up I'd have liked to mention to him the little matter of his friend Brian whose report of swirling flakes at first light had been one of the factors that had decided us against Wintersgill last night. "Oh, didn't Arthur tell you?" Ken replied. "They weren't snowflakes at all. They were bits of shredded newspaper that had blown out of a dustbin."

Spent the afternoon flitting between the church hall and Wintersgill "putting the play to bed," in Ruth's words. Putting it to sleep would have seemed a more apposite metaphor. Margaret, Ken and I did most of the work, with Rachel providing valuable moral support. Still no Arthur, Cora had one of her innumerable committee meetings and not surprisingly Jane didn't show up either, Lesley having advised me this morning that she was now back at uni and planning on spending Christmas with Baz eating jellied slugs on the banks of the Ganges. Nor did Matthew join us, although I wasn't sure whether he'd been lured away by a good football match on Sky Sports, or served with an emergency injunction prohibiting him from going within a two hundred metre radius of any of Lord Buttermere's fixtures and fittings.

Afterwards, Ruth kindly invited us back for an enormous tea. As we ate and drank, Cora asked what contribution I'd be making to the entertainment side of the choir Christmas party in twelve days, and before I could answer I was handed a sheet of paper with a number of ideas. I had to admit I was not ecstatic about any of them, even the ones with my name and accompanying question mark handwritten beside them. But before I could make any excuses, she told me she is suggesting that we charge a little more than usual on the basis of a higher standard of entertainment, with the profit going to the vestry fund. "With family and friends invited as well, we could make quite a bit," she said.

It was a nice thought on her part. I suppose. Then again, I really don't see how in all conscience we can justify making people pay extra to watch Henry Peasgood and Eileeen Crosby's festive interpretation of *Tie Me Kangaroo Down Sport* complete with tinsel-wrapped didgeridoos. And I for one would happily pay out of my own pocket a sum equating to the anticipated profits of the evening specifically to avoid having to team up with Irving Cattermole, Margaret Pardew and Hazel Ledworthy to sing, to the tune of Britten's *Hymn To The Virgin*, the words of the Human Fertilisation And Embryology (Higher Court Rights Of Audience) Part 3 Amendment Regulations 1996.

Friday 12th December

A day off for me, and a lovely day it was as Katie and I went Christmas shopping in Salisbury. It was a deliciously cold, crisp, sunny day, and Katie looked fantastic. I thought back on Margaret's words of twelve days ago and how clearly God had pointed me towards Katie and away from Jane. Over a long lunch in one of the city's many delightful eateries, we talked very seriously about our future, neither of us in any doubt that we wanted to be together for the rest of our lives. After lunch, having found a pretext for going off for a short while on my own, I went to my favourite restaurant in the city, which I'd visited only on very special occasions in the past, and booked a table for two for the evening of Tuesday 23rd December, having resolved that over dinner that night I would ask Katie to be my wife.

After such a great day it was a horrid anticlimax to return home, in fairly ghastly rush-hour traffic, and part company with my lovely fiancée-to-be. Even more hateful was arriving at choir practice and hearing that because of a clash with the children's Christingle and crib service – Joan Trumpington inevitably to blame – our carol service is being moved from the 22nd December to the 23rd. "It gets worse," Tripplehorn went on. "This year the vicar wants us to sing the whole service by candlelight. It'll mean that we will have to sing holding lighted candles all the way through. Try doing that while processing round the church reading from one sheet of music and holding about three books at the same time."

I certainly have no intention of trying, but as Tripplehorn was in a pretty vile mood for much of the evening, I really didn't feel up to telling him that I'm going to have to miss the whole ghastly business. What makes things more awkward is the fact that part of the collection at the carol service will be going to the vestry fund. With Arthur back on the tenor line, even less blendable than usual, I was in no mood to enjoy tonight's practice and when halfway through I was despatched to fetch a couple of extra hymn books from the vestry and could see neither hide or hair of them I really did feel like slipping out via the back door and going home. At length I found the missing volumes, and returned to the stalls as Sunday's music was being distributed. Henry Peasgood looked up at me as I passed him and said "Whose LP is this then?" He repeated this question a couple of times and chuckled, clearly enjoying himself immensely. I was on the point of getting out my mobile to phone for a deputation of kindly men in white coats when he pointed to the piece of music that had just been distributed and said "This is the record of John." If that's how fifteen years of choir membership affect one, I think I'd rather go off and do something more worthwhile and generally less labour intensive. Rumour has it that on the community notice board in Savemart there's a vacancy for vice-chairman of the local branch of the Redmarley D'Abitot Red Telephone Kiosk Preservation Action Group.

Sunday 14th December

What should have been a lovely Advent 3 service this morning, with super music and very moving liturgy, was really quite spoilt for me by the thought of the town carol-singing that was to come at lunchtime. By contrast with eight days ago, it was a very mild but blowy day with a fine patchy drizzle falling from a murky sky.

As Katie and I made our way towards the market hall we were virtually unable to move for the number of people that were thronging the pedestrian precinct. It was, if anything, busier than I would have expected it to be on a Saturday afternoon. Once we were all present, Tripplehorn gave us the first bit of bad news. "There's been a bit of a bodge-up on timings," he announced. "As you know we were asked to sing at one o'clock. But I'm told that because of all the other attractions outside the market hall today, it looks like we won't be on until getting on for two. Sorry about that."

I was all for going and finding a quiet café where we might sit down and while away the intervening forty five minutes but Katie, trying out a pair of brand new boots, seemed singularly reluctant to move in any direction and pointed out that we might in any case be getting on sooner than we thought, especially with the hot news that Tony Toplady, the Concrete Juggler of Three Legged Cross, had brought his act to an unscheduled stop by bringing a standard-size housebrick down on his left foot.

No sooner had he hobbled from the arena, though, than we learned that the chamber of commerce had booked in two more intervening acts before ours, both clearly of equal spiritual significance to the antics of Mr Toplady and just as faithful to the observance of the Sabbath as a day of subdued contemplation and spiritual nourishment: Albert Cocklewick, a stand-up comedian whose repertoire seemed to consist entirely of entries from Volume 28 of *The Oldest And Unfunniest Mother-in-Law Joke Collection* and whose signature comic routine was the hurling of a custard pie in the face of anybody unwise enough to stand within firing distance, and Charlie Crabtree, an impressionist whose repertoire started with a feeble attempt at Frank Spencer and progressed via Harold Wilson and Edward Heath to someone who might have been the Deputy Foreign Secretary of Liechtenstein or the cigarette counter supervisor of the Ashton-under-Lyne branch of KwikSave. At last, however, the rostrum was vacated and we were able to take the stand at a couple of minutes to two. Immediately we did so, the milling hordes that had enthused at the antics of Messrs Toplady, Cocklewick and Crabtree retreated with almost indecent haste. A more efficient job of crowd dispersal could not have been effected by armed Bolivian riot police.

We struggled on, with an audience consisting of a handful of frail pensioners, at least two of whom I recognised from church as the

Oglethorpe sisters whose bladder conditions always render it advisable that they decamp as soon as they have received communion. True to form, they ambled away after ten minutes, during our singularly ropey rendition of *I Saw Three Ships*. Their place was promptly taken by a bearded octogenarian attired in grubby orange pullover, running shorts and mud-splashed plimsolls, and holding a large placard. Suddenly, to our collective discomfiture, he began booming out an incomprehensible message at three hundred decibels that served to sink the trio of vessels of which we had been singing, and threatened to obliterate *Gabriel's Message* altogether. I wondered if perhaps he was the bearer of a prophetic message from the Almighty, pronouncing the nearness of the end time and certain doom for those engaged in commercial activity on this most holy day of the week. Until, that was, I caught sight of the placard, and saw that it was in fact proclaiming a closing-down sale in the Smalls R Us store in Haven Row with eighty per cent discounts off twenty-pair packs of underpants. At length Tripplehorn persuaded him to move on, in terms that would not necessarily have convinced any passer-by that we were representatives of the town's principal place of Christian worship. By then, however, any lingering enthusiasm that we might have had for being stuck here for a second longer than was necessary had ebbed away, so we decided to cut our losses and leave the scene. Our collecting tin, which we would expect to have filled during an evening's carol-singing, was as light as a guide to mangrove swamps around Chalfont St Giles.

I suggested to Katie that we head out of town and enjoy a cosy farmhouse tea at Maggie's Pantry, having first taken the precaution of checking out the availability of hot fluffy cheese scones and home-made chocolate yule log. We had such a lovely time, and the cheese scones were so good, that I hardly liked to tell her that on the 23rd, which I had asked her to keep free for a "special surprise evening," I am now expected to be singing carols at St Basil's. But tell her I did. Katie's response was instantaneous. "Ring Frank Tripplehorn now on your mobile," she said. "Tell him you can't sing at the service. You've busted a gut for this blasted vestry fund. Some of the others can pull their weight for goodness sake. They all just take you for granted. Go on. Show me you're a man."

With thumping heart and knocking knees, I telephoned Tripplehorn straight away. I told him very forcefully that I had an extremely important engagement that night, that logistically there were no huge difficulties in executing the music without me, that the one solo I had been allotted, verse 3 of *In The Bleak Midwinter*, could easily be sung an octave higher by one of the sopranos, that I had given a hundred and ten per cent to the vestry fund during the year, that the job of raising money for the fund was not reserved exclusively to me, and that I was simply asking for this one small indulgence during the season of goodwill. A few moments later our conversation ended.

"Well?" Katie demanded.

"He's – er – going to reallocate verse 3 of *In The Bleak Midwinter*," I replied.

"There you are," said Katie. "Bit of assertiveness. That's all it took."

I honestly hadn't the heart, or the stomach, to reveal that while I had lost that verse, I had just gained verse 3 of *It Came Upon The Midnight Clear*, verse 2 of *Jesus Christ The Apple Tree*, the first tenor line of the semi-chorus in Rutter's *Angel Tidings*, and the upper line in the second tenor part in the first 15 bars of verse 11 of the first choir performance since 1947 of *Carol To The Moon* by Dr Barnabas Tolleshunt-Partington.

Friday 19ᵗʰ December

A predictably dire rehearsal this evening, practising for Advent 4 as well as the carol service and the music for the midnight service. To his credit, Tripplehorn did not dwell on anything for very long, but it was still a hard sing and I would have been happy to have missed the party which followed, especially as Katie was working and could not come along. But since a proportion of the entrance money was going to the fund, as Cora had suggested twelve days ago, and I was making a small contribution to the first half of the entertainment, I had no choice but to stay. As party organiser, Cora had obviously gone to a lot of trouble to put a varied programme together. But after Henry Peasgood's struggle through a Stanley Holloway monologue, and Craig Dumbleton's home-grown poem of dubious merit about a childhood visit to Santa's grotto in Hartlepool, delivered in cod Geordie accent, I saw the whole evening going down the toilet faster than a squirt of Mr Muscle U-bend unblocker. And while it was nice of Cora to secure for me a non-singing, non-dancing, invisible role cocooned in blissful anonymity and generous warmth, I can think of pleasanter ways of passing a Friday evening than dressing myself up as the back legs of the pantomime horse in Cora's brother's one-man version of *Cinderella And The Beanstalk*.

By the time we reached the food interval, I had had enough and, having made an excuse about an urgent work project, went home. I checked for messages on my answering machine and found there was one from a Brian Blackmore asking me to call him urgently on his mobile. The name meant nothing to me and my first thought was to leave it till tomorrow morning, but it was still only ten and I decided to return the call then relax with scrambled eggs and a decent late-night TV talk show. It was thus to my annoyance that I found that all he wanted to know was the email and telephone contact for ordering Arthur's wretched book. Since he made it quite clear he didn't personally want a copy, and even if he did want one we are still set to make a whopping loss on the project, it was with some asperity that I gave him the information.

"One other thing," he said. "Can people actually get copies on line?" I curtly told him we didn't have the facility for anyone to do that.

"Might be worth thinking about," he said. "Cheerio."

I thought about it, then turned to the more pressing matter of my scrambled eggs. I suspect that the only goods any of the purchasers of Arthur's book have ever attempted to obtain on line are likely to have been the perch fished from Paradise Pond at the end of Pleasant Street. Well, before Craggs Pesticides dumped three lorry loads of toxic waste into it, anyway.

Sunday 21st December

A quite astonishing turn of events. Had returned home yesterday evening after a busy day out doing my final bits of Christmas shopping with Katie, to find no less than fifty email requests for copies of Arthur's book, and a further eleven orders on my answering machine. On further enquiry, I had ascertained that the book had been mentioned in a feature on BBC local radio earlier in the day entitled "The Year's Worst" in which every conceivable category of awfulness was explored in the context of the past year's events. The most tedious politician, the worst excesses of bureaucracy, the worst example of public service, the most irritating TV personality, and so on. One category had apparently been "The Most Boring Book" and the announcer had said something like "And I guarantee that this book of choir goings-on somewhere in southern England will have sent you to sleep by the end of the contents page." The announcer had then gone on to discuss Arthur's book in some detail and, "for all those saddos who can't resist seeing for themselves how bad it is," gave all the contact details I'd given Brian Blackmore on the Friday evening.

But there was more. Naturally I'd rung Brian Blackmore, who it turned out was the man who'd expressed such interest in the book at Arthur's signing session last month, and I asked him if it was he that was responsible for all the free publicity. He admitted that he had indeed passed the story on to the radio programme, and as a direct result of that programme the national press had taken an interest. And when I arrived at church this morning I was presented with a copy of not one but two of the Sunday papers, one running the story as a news item and the other including a review of the book in their arts pages. The news item quoted verbatim from the radio reviewer who had talked at length about how this had to be the worst book of its kind he had ever read but "its sheer awfulness has a kind of nobility that somehow forces you to read on. You keep on willing the anecdotes to get funnier and richer but the overall effort becomes not dissimilar to that of trying to get out of the Hampton Court maze five minutes before closing at the same time as consuming a bowl of soup with a fish slice, your sense of optimism being overtaken by a feeling of total impotence and ultimate acceptance of inevitable submission." Perversely, the reviewer, and of course the journalist who was quoting from him, were actually giving the book huge curiosity value which I guessed would prove to be a major selling point and create a very considerable demand.

After an enjoyable morning's service – in a ridiculous sort of way I felt quite elated as we sang Holst's *Lullay My Liking* – I was absolutely bombarded with book orders from members of the congregation. Arthur, apparently totally unfazed by being labelled such an incompetent writer, seemed to be in his element as he signed copy after copy. I got home to find at least another eighty orders on email, another dozen or so telephone orders, and urgent requests from a number of bookshops, including the sales director of one of the biggest bookshop chains in Southern England, to supply copies at once. Katie, bless her, was most understanding that our planned return to Maggie's Pantry for their speciality thickly-iced Christmas cake had to be cancelled in order for me to parcel up copies for all those who'd placed orders by email and telephone, and to make arrangements for a further print run with Roger Endacott to be undertaken tomorrow morning. Then, when I delivered a hefty consignment of copies to our bookshop in town, Peter Collingsworth the manager told me to expect not only a good many more orders but a call from a publisher who is interested in buying our rights in the book and could well pay us a substantial lump sum for them. When I asked how much, Mr Collingsworth replied "Let's just say enough not only for the vestry fund but maybe a new set of choir robes too."

By the time I fell into bed, exhausted, we seemed on target not only to pay for a new vestry and new set of choir robes, but some half-decent music folders, a complete set of new Oxford anthem books which Tripplehorn has been desperate to obtain for months, Royal School Of Church Music life membership, and ten years' worth of choir outings complete with bulging picnic hampers and new camcorder for Arthur Ramsbottom. With perhaps just enough left to keep Henry Peasgood in Fisherman's Friends for as long as he had it in him.

Tuesday 23rd December

Fortunately I was able to get another day off work today, and having taken delivery of the boxes of extra copies that Roger Endacott had somehow produced in barely 36 hours, I spent the day delivering parcels of books to all the shops within reach, and arranging couriers for the stores I couldn't get to, so anxious was I to honour as many orders as I could before the Christmas break. Yesterday I'd had a couple of magazines take an interest as well, so there seemed every chance that the momentum would continue after the festive season.

Then towards lunchtime I got a call on my mobile from a Mark McIntyre who told me that his London publishing firm wished to purchase the rights to the book. It seems they plan to do a reprint, using their own media contacts to keep the interest going, then when demand slackens, they intend to incorporate the more dire sections of the book into an "anthology of awfulness." Although final arrangements won't be confirmed until well into the New Year, it looks as though the money we'll make from it will, as Mr Collingsworth predicted, be more than enough for the vestry fund.

Frankly the last thing I wanted to do, I thought to myself as I arrived home at six thirty in a state of exhaustion, was to take part in tonight's carol service. I'd rung the vicar and suggested that it would be inappropriate in all the circumstances for the collection money to go to the vestry fund, and advocated that we donate it to a deserving children's charity instead. My motives weren't entirely selfless, for I had a plan to ring Tripplehorn, and, doing my best impression of a stuffed hedgehog with bronchitis, tell him I wasn't up to it tonight. A plan that collapsed in ruins when the telephone rang as soon as I got in, and having answered it in my normal voice, I found it was none other than Tripplehorn himself. "Arthur and Craig are both unwell," he said, "so you've got verse 3 of *In The Bleak Midwinter* back. See you in ten minutes."

Although it was a nuisance to have to go out, I was glad I did, for not only were there several book orders which I might otherwise have missed out on, but there was also a superbly large congregation, numbers undoubtedly boosted by all the book publicity. However, the service itself was not a success. The vicar's seasonal witticisms had at least moved away from the hitherto perennial promise of "mulled pie and minced wine" afterwards, to announcements to the effect that we would be singing *In The BMW*, *Away In A Manager* and Rutter's *Shepherd's Pie Carol*. Things were not improved by Henry Peasgood, during *God Rest You Merry Gentlemen*, thundering at two hundred decibels "in tempest storm and wined" despite clear instructions by Tripplehorn that "wind" was to be given its normal pronunciation; Matthew dropping all his music on at least three occasions during the proceedings including on the line "how silently, how silently" in the carol *O Little Town Of Bethlehem*; Tripplehorn changing his mind so many times about who was to sing which verses of the Taize carol we were performing that what had started with two sopranos singing verse 2 pianissimo ended up with a double forte rendition joined in not only by the entire soprano section but the altos, tenors and basses, the entire congregation, and the satellite-linked massed voices of the Huddersfield Choral Society and the City of Adelaide Philharmonic Choir; and Zoe's opening verse of *Once In Royal* sharpening so much with every line that the rest of us could only feel sorry we hadn't brought our blunt HB pencils.

Afterwards I asked Tripplehorn what he thought of the evening. "Frankly," he said, "I'm only too glad we weren't reliant on the collection for the vestry fund. Since if their donations tonight were based on the quality of our performance, we'd have been lucky to raise enough to cover the vicar's proper prefaces."

I couldn't have put it better myself.

Wednesday 24th December

Spent the evening at my home with Katie, enjoying a superb home-cooked lasagne, chuckling at the first hour of the *One Hundred Greatest TV Soap Christmas Moments*, and discussing where we might go for a week away early next month, when Katie has no catering bookings and I've a few days owing to me too. I was determined to treat us both to a really lovely romantic holiday, during which I would ask her to be my wife. That, I decided, would more than make up for the disappointment of losing out on our big meal in Salisbury last night. We had just decided on the week 4th-11th January when I got a phone call from Mr Trimble, the PCC secretary.

"Sorry to disturb you so close to Christmas," he said. "But I realised that on the next PCC agenda you're down to present a report about the vestry fund appeal and announce the provisional sum raised. I just want to make sure you'll be there for it. It's January 6th."

I suppose the weather can be very unpredictable during the first week in January. Flights will be just as cheap the following week. And all things considered, with 44 items on the agenda, I could have found myself a lot worse off than item 33. But I really can't blame Katie for allowing her jaw to drop faster than sales of St George flags after England's latest penalty shoot-out defeat.

As we made our way to church for the midnight service, I felt totally deflated. By a strangely ironic twist she was wearing just the same outfit that had attracted me to her so much when I had seen her in the church exactly a year ago, and she looked, if anything, even more gorgeous tonight. I had no doubt that her new-found commitment to Christ had served to make her even brighter, more confident and more captivating than she had been twelve months before. She caused heads to turn whenever I went out with her. She deserved someone really special: if not a handsome fairytale prince, then maybe a gallant soldier or a sporting hero. She did not deserve a sad geek whose idea of an evening out was waiting for item 33 sub paragraph (b) on a badly typed agenda.

But once the service had got under way, a strange and powerful determination replaced the feeling of hopelessness, a determination that seemed to be reinforced rather than quenched by the message of love and hope of the Nativity. It was truly as though God had chosen this holiest of holy nights to reach out His loving arms towards me. As the service progressed, the way forward suddenly became clear and I realised it did not require a flight to a faraway destination or an expensive dinner. So it was that after the service, I asked Katie to come with me to the crib below the plain glass south window, this being the very spot on which a year ago, I had felt God's presence more powerfully than at any other time in my life, and therefore the perfect place to invite her to share the rest of her life with me. There, with the moon shining into the south transept from the starlit sky, I asked her to be my wife.

She looked deep into my eyes. "I'd love to marry you," she said, placing a huge kiss on my lips.

Slowly, we made our way out of the church. The congregation had all disappeared and we found ourselves on our own, walking arm in arm down the church path beneath the stars.

"Just promise me one thing," Katie half whispered to me. "You will stop all this fundraising nonsense now, won't you?"

"I promise," I said.

And as she enveloped me in her arms, I could almost see a veil being lifted to reveal a tiny piece of glorious eternity and a magical vision of our Father's wisdom and purpose for each one of His earthly children.

Which perhaps meant it wasn't the ideal time to tell Katie that inside the Christmas card the vicar had handed me in the vestry tonight was a request to form and head up a steering committee tasked with financing the restoration and repair and, if necessary, replacement of the two clapped-out churchyard grass-cutting appliances.

Sunday 28th December

Despite the fact that my fiancée had decided she could do with a long lie-in after a late liquid night at the Holly Tree, she nobly agreed to accompany me to St Basil's this morning to hear the official announcement of the success of the vestry appeal. All being well, work on the project should be able to commence as early as February. Although, as Margaret would quite rightly remind me, the glory should really go to God, I couldn't help feeling just a little bit proud of myself as we made our way up the path.

Unfortunately, anticlimax soon set in. A number of choir members were away including Ken, the Ellises, the Sparkes, Margaret and Eileen. Moreover, the vicar wasn't there either, and we found ourselves in the not-so-very-capable hands of Lawrence Doubtfire who Lesley reckoned had been pensioned off by the Church of England about 120 years ago. Tripplehorn very philosophical about it, saying that he would fill any awkward pause by slipping in one of the eight carols we'd not got to during communion at the midnight mass. I was, however, all too conscious of having dragged Katie along specially to hear the announcement about the appeal, and was seriously concerned that Doubtfire would forget to mention it. Accordingly, I made a beeline for Tony Smart, who's been acting as churchwarden owing to the illness of one of the incumbents, and asked him if he could make sure it was announced. "I'll do my best," Tony responded. "Mind you, it's taken about half an hour's coaching to get him to intone the opening of the Gloria."

The service proceeded. Tripplehorn was as good as his word, and with Doubtfire's celebration of the Eucharist peppered with unscheduled hiatuses, unforced errors and occasional double faults, I think we'd whizzed through most if not all of the *Bethlehem Carol Sheet* and were already starting the second lap by the time the surprisingly large congregation had received communion. As for the vestry fund announcement, I could only guess that the task had proved beyond Tony in the time available, for when we reached the notices, there was no mention of it at all. But even as I was thinking how to frame my apology to Katie afterwards, I was suddenly aware of Doubtfire stopping halfway through the words of dismissal and choosing to announce it then. In fairness to him, he thanked me quite effusively, despite mispronouncing my name, and I felt about ten feet tall as I saw the St Basil's faithful favouring me with expressions of genuine warmth and gratitude. "So," Doubtfire concluded, "I invite you to join me in applauding his efforts and wishing a very happy and successful New Year to the lucky charity – the St Leodegar's School Minibus Appeal."

At least there was no mention of the dodgy lawnmowers.

Wednesday 31st December

"You've not opened this letter," Katie said, passing to me a brown envelope bearing my name. I swallowed the last of my coffee and opened the envelope. Inside was a letter from the church treasurer to the effect that as the local paper's photographer had an unexpected window tomorrow afternoon, could I convene the choir for a group photo, with me at the front handing over a giant cheque for the money now guaranteed for the vestry fund.

"Well, I think you ought to do it," said Katie, downing the rest of her tea. "You will say yes, won't you?"

I hesitated. In my mind's eye I suddenly pictured the probable calamities that would befall me if I dared to take such a step, based on my experience of the year that had passed. If we chose an outdoor venue we would be beaten back inside either by sweltering heat or a typhoon or possibly both, while if we went indoors we would find ourselves facing eviction by an irate caretaker telling us he needed the room for the January meeting of the town's Synchronised Moroccan Fancy Needlework class. The cheque would probably never reach us in the first place, having been entrusted to Joan Trumpington's tender care and placed in a brown paper parcel bound for Upton Snodsbury. The presentation would be hijacked by Ruth Hartnell who would insist on postponing it, forming a subcommittee and calling a series of evening meetings that would mean I missed the first three editions of Channel Five's new peaktime show, *Celebrity Bookshelf Dusting*. Craig Dumbleton would have had to present his apologies on the pretext of a long-standing engagement to address the annual meeting of the Catford Station Booking Office Ticket Window Appreciation Society. Henry Peasgood, on observing the scene, would comment that he had raised ten times as much money on Comic Relief Day in 1988 by singing all 548 hymns in the *New English Hymnal* to the tune Gonfalon Royal. Irving Cattermole would have remembered he'd promised to grout his first cousin's second wife's shower unit in Flyford Flavell. Matthew Sparkes would insert a handful of itching powder down the back of Eileen Crosby's dress just before she posed for the camera. Hazel Ledworthy would look disdainfully on the whole scene with a stare as frigid as the water in the Haverfordwest Bus Station gents' toilet at the dawn of the new Ice Age. And Arthur Ramsbottom would, of course, be studiously camcording and noting every last detail for volume 75 of his newly enlarged choir history, including such indispensable information as the kind of cereal consumed by the cameraman for his breakfast that morning, the respective sock colours and patterns of those sitting in the front row, and precise percentages of those who at the time the picture was taken were smiling, blinking, grimacing or picking at their nasal hairs.

I took a deep breath and gazed out of the window. Above, a crystal clear blue sky and a cold but breathtakingly bright winter sun. Below, the snow-capped Tyrolean mountain peaks, standing guard over majestic forests and cosy villages, beckoning us to our New Year retreat and already defying us not to sense the luscious aromas of Kaffee und Kuchen and Wiener schnitzel. I snuggled up comfortably into the deepest recesses of my seat as the plane slowly began its descent towards our very own winter wonderland, then considered Katie's question.

"I think I might just give it a miss," I said.

THE END